MW00577304

Healing Against The Odds by Leslie Peake is a resource for just what the title says. I learned, as a surgeon caring for cancer patients, that there was survival behavior. Leslie's book identifies all the factors which helped her become what my wife called, an Exceptional Cancer Patient. I learned that when people didn't die when they were supposed to they all had a story to tell about how and why it happened. Leslie's book outlines this step by step as she evolves and lets her body know she now chooses life and is creating a new self. With faith, hope and love amazing things can happen. When your body gets a live message your internal chemistry changes and self healing can be induced by the transformation, harmony and willingness to go through the labor pains of self-birthing your new self free of disease. Read and learn from Leslie; she makes a great coach. Doctors talk about spontaneous remissions but it isn't spontaneous. It is about change and work so let Leslie guide and manage your self induced healing and performance too.

— BERNIE SIEGEL, *MD NYTIMES BESTSELLER AUTHOR OF LOVE, MEDICINE & MIRACLES, PEACE, LOVE & HEALING AND MORE.*

Leslie's book is a wonderful inspiration to me, my colleagues, and others. This book addresses not only people dealing with a health crisis. All of us are at risk to suffer from an unhealthy condition, therefore I think it's for everyone. It contains poetry, wisdom, practical knowledge and inspiration. This book is a remedy!

— ANGELA WEISS, *NATUROPATHIC THERAPIST, AUTHOR*

In my forty-some years of clinical practice you get to learn from a multitude of different people, but only very few leave a lasting impression. One of these special personalities is the author of this book. She has taught us and with this book will certainly educate many others, how a shocking diagnosis can positively intensify your life and deliver love, forgiveness, trust, compassion and gratitude.

— JOHN VAN LIMBURG STIRUM, *MD.*

Leslie's book has inspired me, kept me going when I didn't think I had anything left. Leslie is the definition of inspiration. Thank you for all the awareness you have given me through reading your book. This is a must read for anyone with an illness of any kind.

— BARBARA ANNE PLATT, *RHEUMATOID ARTHRITIS SURVIVOR*

This book reaches out as a voice of hope for healing not only the body, but also the soul. Peake pulls from a deep well of personal experience and professional expertise to speak to people diagnosed with cancer in a language that rings true to them. She speaks from her own soul to the reader's soul. And yet, her work is so firmly grounded in the body. I most appreciated the "Soul Activation Exercises," which offer concrete ways to look within and get real about why you want to live, how you want to live, what you need to let go of, and how to get started manifesting the life within you that still wants to be lived. A beautiful wisdom flows from every page.

— KATIE SEGGERSON, *CANCER SURVIVOR &
THRIVER, JUNGIAN ANALYST IN TRAINING*

Leslie's book is a must read for anyone who wants to discover the ingredients for a more authentic and healthy life. She invites the reader into her life and shares how her journey has taught her to live not only as a survivor of cancer but as a "thriver." Leslie's vulnerability shines through as she shares her innermost personal practice of embracing each day through the lens of hope and healing. As a counselor, mother, skin cancer thriver, and a wife to someone with cancer, I recommend this book to you as her work positively impacts my own life daily.

— MICHELLE CLOSE, *SCHOOL COUNSELOR*

From the start of her arduous ordeal, I have observed with incredulity Leslie's determination not only to fight for her life but to remain open to what her struggle had to offer her; this book recounts her journey with the same grace, strength, and focus she employed to get through it. Her newfound wisdom is an inspirational gift to the rest of us.

— DENISE HAZEN, *EDUCATIONAL COACH*

Leslie has inspired me throughout my own journey of life. She is a holistic person in the way she thinks, behaves and relates to people. It is no wonder that she is sharing her life experience with cancer the way she is doing in her book. She questions, she seeks information, and she keeps on going until it makes sense. It is all about sharing her experience in the hope to inspire those around her to always keep on seeking what feels right for them. Every story offers learning, Leslie awards us hers.

— RUTH FORMOSA VENTURA,
PSYCHOTHERAPIST

HEALING AGAINST THE ODDS:

HOW TO RISE UP FROM THE ASHES OF CANCER

LESLIE PEAKE

Red Thread Publishing LLC. 2022

Write to info@redthreadbooks.com if you are interested in publishing with Red Thread Publishing. Learn more about publications or foreign rights acquisitions of our catalogue of books: www.redthreadbooks.com

Paperback ISBN : 978-1-955683-08-1

Ebook ISBN : 978-1-955683-17-3

Cover Design: Andrea Schmidt

WRITE.PUBLISH.IMPACT.
Red Thread Publishing

I dedicate this book to all people whose lives have been touched by cancer.

CONTENTS

Part II
CONNECTION

Part III

EMERGENCE

FOREWORD

*"A passage through the door of the heart." Can there
be any more meaningful journey?*

In her book, Leslie Peake shares with us her journey of
discovery, an opening of the heart towards reality and
healing, that is a gift for all. She readily embraces the
vulnerability of uncertainty, not knowing, triggered by the
realization of having cancer in her body. Her journey touches
the fragility and despair that is part of the human experience
and that provides, for those who are brave and willing, the
opportunity to enter inner stillness, profound knowing, and
the process of opening the heart.

It is with sincere humility and curiosity that Leslie shares
and reveals the stages of her passage and discoveries. Her
insights constitute a path, a hopeful one, especially for the
many of us who have and who will suffer quietly and alone
with the travails of cancer.

The illumination of the path that Leslie offers us involves
facing fear, integrating uncertainty, and letting the process

lead to insight and understanding, and love that enhances our inner healing and common humanity. We the reader are invited to journey with Leslie on her exploration of what it means to live with and open to our fragility and inner strength. There is no other more important journey.

The soul evolution that Leslie elucidates is a path that opens towards healing, a set of guideposts that identify stages of the path, and a map of the inner world of the body and mind that is available for each of us. This path is a possibility not only for people who have been touched by cancer, but also for all of us who have a wish to face vulnerability and awakening. Her insights are informed by her own deep experiencing and willingness to dive into the dark night of the soul.

Instead of avoiding reality and suffering, it is clear that Leslie has chosen to dive full on into the depths of reality and suffering with a clear motivation to learn the depth of our human capacity. The amazing result of her inquiry is what she elucidates here in her offering to the world, to each of us, to paint a picture of what is possible even in the context of great physical and emotional suffering.

The challenge now for the reader is how to implement the pearls of wisdom and insight Leslie has painstakingly unearthed in her own journey. Importantly, it behooves each one of us to understand that healing from cancer after medical treatments is a personal journey that requires carving out a path that transcends the medical model of treating symptoms. In fact, it requires an open holistic perspective on what healing means.

This is a personal journey to see clearly one's own capacity to live with pain and suffering, with self-kindness, with respect for the suffering of others, and to cultivate one's own wisdom and insight and love for oneself. If nothing else, Leslie's book serves to inspire one to do this journey of healing.

I have had the great honor to have Leslie as a friend, to witness her inner strength, her thirst to share with and support others. There is a saying in Tibetan that is translated as "transforming adversity or suffering into the path to awakening." This spiritual alchemy is fundamental to well-being.

Each of us has this capacity to transform pain and suffering into penetrating and transformational insight. Leslie's soul evolution is pinpointing one way to do this hard and meaningful work toward self-illumination and transcendent love.

Again, as Leslie states so clearly, "a passage through the door of the heart." Can there be any more meaningful journey?

Philippe Goldin, PhD; he/him/his
Professor. Director, Clinically Applied Affective
Neuroscience Laboratory at University of California Davis

ACKNOWLEDGMENTS

66 We can not do great things

In this world

We can only do small things

With great love.

— MOTHER TERESA

Healing Against the Odds is my small contribution to the vast ocean of writers who have gone before me making it possible for me to share my story. I knew deep inside my heart I had an important story to share and I tried to get it onto paper working alone with the encouragement of family and friends.

Writing a book is another kind of marathon that takes perseverance, dedication, and a fierce commitment to a bigger goal. I realized early on that manifesting this book goes beyond writing just for myself; it is a small act of great love that needs to be shared with others in the world.

Forging ahead alone was not working and it was only when I discovered Red Thread Publishing, founded by Sierra Melcher and her team of amazing women that I began to gain some traction in developing the book. As a first-time author, I knew nothing of what lay ahead that I needed to do and how to stay on track. The project is so much bigger than I imagined and without the constant support from my publishing manager, Doriana Vitti I would still be trying to figure out what my next tasks were to do.

I've had wonderful editorial support in the beginning from Felicity Kuyper who intuitively knew how to help me shape my story by weaving together all the writing I had done since the beginning of my cancer journey. As my manuscript was being completed, Dr. Adrienne Maclain was there to guide me to completion. Without these two amazing women, I would still be treading water trying to find my way.

I am so grateful to my family and close friends who have continued to believe in my dream of writing this book. There are too many of you to name, but you know who you are and without your continuous belief in me, this project would've been a lonely path. My deepest gratitude goes out to each and every one of you, from my heart to yours. I always believe: together, we are stronger. Miracles happen when we believe everything is possible.

Just as this book has taken many people's support to write and publish, I sincerely hope that you as my reader will share this book with many of your loved ones and all those for whom you think my story can make a difference. I want it to be shared, and I can't do all the sharing alone. I'm grateful for your willingness to pass along my story with the hope it will help others along their journey of life.

INTRODUCTION

 May your challenge be led by effortless Qi flow and guide you to your pilgrimage of Liberation.

I know your book will bring a lot of benefit to all who are ready to receive your Light of wisdom.

— TSULTIM NAMDAK, CERTIFIED SHENG ZHEN TEACHER

The news came as a total surprise to me as I sat in the specialist's office, listening to a stranger deliver the most devastating news of my life to me. He showed me a picture of the healthy part of my colon and then moved towards the black, deformed mass that was lodged at the very end of my colon in the rectum and said this collection of cell tissue is cancerous.

His words landed in my consciousness like an unknown landscape that I knew nothing about. I did not cry. I was frozen. Finally, I stood up and went around to look at the monitor that showed a black area, where he said the tumor was.

This is how I found out colorectal cancer was the diagnosis of my colonoscopy.

At this moment, it's a strange mental leap to go from looking at a picture of a part of my body that is showing up as unhealthy cell growth to labeling it as cancer and then owning it as a part of my body. While the evidence was clear, how to make sense of it, was another process altogether.

There were three of us in the doctor's office; our school nurse who insisted she come with my husband and me. I was so thankful she was there because I did not know what to do. I asked what my next step was, having no idea where to turn to and especially living abroad in Switzerland as an expat. She was the one to begin asking questions about the next steps for treatment and specialist options.

I was suspended in time, I was in the room, but not fully there, heading off in my thoughts: *"This is unbelievable, yet I know it to be true, so how do I deal with this new reality?"*

I was rapidly preparing for a new chapter in my life, one that was totally unknown to me. How am I going to navigate this? I know it's not going to be done alone because clearly, I need help! Help on lots of levels, physical being the most prominent one at the moment.

Mental, emotional, and spiritual support were also calling me. I was ready to rally up the teams even though I didn't know who they were going to be or what any of it would look like. I was open to all possibilities.

He went on to tell me in the kindest way possible that, if it was him, he would immediately go and get all of his rectum removed. I had no idea what this meant nor what it would look like in my body. This thought, as foreign to me as receiving this diagnosis, was not a helpful one to share.

Thankfully, my dear friend who is also a skillful and knowledgeable nurse was able to provide a way forward with the best team of medical specialists she could find. I was suddenly flung into a new reality that was terrifying and yet finally provided a direction for me.

My story begins long before this meeting, but this was the point when the initial diagnosis became real and my life took the biggest, unexpected turn that even I couldn't have imagined. The start of a new road opened up before me and as Saki Santorelli eloquently says, I had to "reckon with the challenge of taking back my life and the effort required to awaken to the fullness of this one life I have to live."

"I asked myself, why did I go for so long in so much discomfort? "

I reflected back on the things that led up to my final decision to get a colonoscopy. I did have stomach aches, digestive problems, and tiredness that became more extreme as the months passed.

My joyful energy and patience for others became thin and I began to notice I just didn't feel like myself. Yoga, meditation, walks in the woods, taking more vitamins, getting more sleep, nothing seemed to have an impact on how I was feeling. I dragged myself into work every day until finally I just couldn't think clearly anymore nor have the energy to make it through a workday.

Something had to give.

It was December of 2014 when I first started noticing a slight change in my digestion. The awareness was very subtle, yet something inside me said, 'there is something different with me.' Changes can come at first, very quietly, and then if we don't listen to them, they get progressively louder.

And so it was, with time I noticed a difference in my digestion and a slight change in my bowel movements. I heard a dim voice trying to get my attention and I did notice it, yet I did not do anything about it or bother to tell anyone.

Mentally, I swept it under the carpet.

I've learned that if your body has always been functioning one way and then it starts to change, this is something to pay attention to regardless of a past, healthy history.

This is where my thinking closed in on me, once healthy, always healthy!

It seemed so insignificant and perhaps because I have never had anything wrong with me physically, I thought it would eventually pass. I was 52 and in perimenopause and I thought this might be a change connected to my stage of life.

I've always considered myself a healthy person who exercised regularly and was active in sports my whole life. I was the one carefully reading ingredients on the food labels of what I was buying as I wanted to feed my children the "cleanest" foods possible.

I taught yoga and mindfulness to kids and adults and had a daily practice of both for myself. Anyone who knows me would never suspect anything would be wrong with me health-wise and it never occurred to me that something terribly off-balance was brewing in my body.

Looking back I can now see that I was in denial of the changes that my body was showing me because I was convinced I had done everything right in terms of making good food and lifestyle choices.

I continued to notice for a whole year more subtle signs of something not-quite-right. The feeling never left me that my digestion and bowel movements were not acting the way they usually did.

Again, because I have always been healthy, never in the hospital for anything other than two natural childbirths. My thoughts never went to thinking there may be something really wrong with me.

When I turned fifty years old, both kids were now living in Canada going to university, so I assumed my life would get easier. Less laundry, cleaning, cooking, helping to coordinate family schedules. Yet I found myself more tired, more harried, and more exhausted. I thought the "empty nesting" would be a welcome break from the 20-year cycle of day-to-day parenting.

As I look back, I now wonder if the busyness I made of parenting and taking care of others became a distraction for what was going on inside me? Parenting and working full time can easily be all-consuming. I see how I allowed the endless demands from the outside world and the expectations I placed on myself to be a good, conscious parent and school counselor fill up my life.

I think it's important to have a picture of what else was going on at the time leading up to my diagnosis because it was part of the whole picture that contributed to how I was perceiving my state of health and unconsciously supporting a growing storm inside.

About a full year later after first noticing something off with my digestion and increasing difficulty with regular bowel movements, symptoms started to show up with more intensity. My energy levels were becoming less and less, it was really an effort for me to make dinner after working every day and my interest in food was diminishing.

Then it became hard to stand up while I was making dinner because there was increasing pressure in my lower abdomen and pelvic floor area so I found myself grabbing a stool to sit on while I prepared food. This became a new nightly habit that I gave into. I thought it was a bit much that I physically had to sit down to find a pain-free position to continue working, but again, I found a way to carry on with my daily routine. As soon as dinner was finished, I was laying on the couch for the rest of the evening and soon fell asleep.

I was losing weight and for most women, that's usually not such a bad thing thinking I could drop a few kilos anyway. As I go back through this in my mind, I'm wondering to myself, why didn't I do something more at this point. Clearly, this was not my normal self, and wasn't this a clue that more was going on in my body that needed some help?

Yes, it was a big clue. However, I had conditioned myself to plow forward, to just keep going without stopping to question too hard what I was doing. For so many years working and raising a family this was the approach that kept me going for better or worse. I had an unconscious goal to be the best I could be, for my family, for myself, that I wasn't even fully aware of how much it was driving me.

It was these subtle, unconscious patterns of thinking and deep-seated beliefs that got in the way of truly seeing the reality of the present moment and what was actually going on for me.

My job at the time was very busy and I had a lot of responsibilities. It took everything I had and more to keep my own stress levels down. I started to feel like I couldn't keep up, no matter what I did to help myself, I never was able to regain an inner vital force of energy where I felt refueled and ready for the next day.

Each day, the layers of exhaustion became greater.

These new levels of exhaustion slowly expanded over time and made it hard for me to separate what was just tiredness from work and what was this other different kind of tiredness that just never went away.

I started having thoughts of, *"How can I get out of this?"* I didn't know how to get off this fast-moving train. My body felt weak like my spine could not hold me up anymore.

I began to realize that it had been so long since I felt deep energy. I thought, is this what it means to be getting older? Because if so, it sucks!

You might be thinking to yourself reading this, why didn't she go to her doctor? We moved to Switzerland without our children when I turned fifty. The pressure to get a doctor was off because I had no kids to take care of and again, what's the rush, I'm healthy.

When I did try to find a house doctor, they were always full. So, I never did secure a new doctor for myself until I was in an acute health crisis. Note to self, it is precisely when you turn fifty that health prevention really needs to kick in and it's time to double up on self-care prevention!

I did go to a gynecologist for a full check-up in February of 2016 and she then referred me to a gastroenterologist who I went to see in March. I decided after seeing both specialists that I would try taking some natural products for easing constipation for a while longer to see if the symptoms would subside. As I had no indicators or risk signs for colon cancer, I put off doing a Colonoscopy at this time.

I added more fiber to my diet and tried various products to help move food through the colon. Nothing really made a difference, though.

I started searching online about menopausal symptoms and found out that constipation can be a real problem for some women going through menopause. I had never heard of this before and I thought to myself, *"This is me! I've figured it out. This must be how menopause is showing up for me."* I wasn't alone with this discomfort and pain!

I found a natural product for constipation and started taking it. It helped a bit. Finally, I had found something that worked. It wasn't perfect, but there was some movement. This eased my mind for a while thinking that I had found something to finally get me back on track.

At this point, I was feeling more desperate to find a solution to the storm that was now quickly gaining momentum.

I continued to go to my upper school counseling job at an international school in Switzerland where every day I felt more and more exhausted.

Then one day, instead of going to my office, I went directly to our school nurse and said, "I can't think, I can't do this anymore!" I hit a wall and could not mentally function. My body was on some kind of altered autopilot. When my mind went to mush, that was the breaking point for me.

She immediately got me in to see any doctor that would take me that day for a blood test. The next day, the results came back showing extremely low iron levels, bordering on anemic. In one way, I was relieved to see it was low and this made sense as to why I had such a deep and unrelenting mental and physical tiredness and exhaustion.

Right away, I received five shots of iron of 100mg each, two per week. After the first week, I could feel my mental energy coming back a bit. I had some capacity to think and work.

Naively, I was hopeful that this was the root of my exhaustion and digestive upsets. I didn't pursue to dig any deeper medically and nor did this doctor. I later learned that one needs to ask more questions to find out why the iron is low, especially now with a year behind me of unusual physical symptoms.

The end of school was approaching and the focus turned towards finishing up school tasks. Going away with a group of students was one of the many things that happen at this time. This year, I was going with the boys' soccer team and three girls to Sri Lanka for 9 days.

My energy had continued to go downhill and I was concerned about how I was going to manage such a trip and be of any help to the group. It never entered my mind that I should drop out from the trip. I would find a way to get through it.

School finished and the summer break was an open road before me. We had planned holidays that were flexible and close by. I was hoping this would be my opportunity to rest, heal, and get my energy and body back to "normal" functioning.

August approached and after 6 weeks of being outside enjoying some biking and hiking, I was feeling healthier than when I finished school. I was hopeful that upon returning, life would fall back into a manageable routine.

However, this was not to be.

As soon as I returned in the first week, all of my previous symptoms came back only this time like a hurricane. I had so much pressure in my pelvic area and perineum, I physically could not stand up without a great deal of pain.

My body was speaking to me loud and clear this time! There was no ignoring the signals.

I immediately went back to the doctor I had seen earlier to get another blood test and a referral for a colonoscopy. It was obvious to me that whatever I had was not going away and now it was worse. I had to find out what was going on and a colonoscopy was the first obvious exam to have.

The colonoscopy was painful for me. I've never had one before so I thought this was normal. I later learned that you shouldn't feel pain and the recovery from having this done is immediate, unlike myself, where I had to sit at home for a couple of days recovering.

However, I still was not worried that I might have cancer. It just never entered my mind. I'm also not the type of person who goes searching around on the internet to do self-diagnosis, so I waited for my follow-up appointment with the doctor.

Since discovering that I was not immune to getting a serious illness, I have read about many people like myself getting cancer: healthy and active, with no family history of cancer and yet this is also boggling the minds of doctors as well. Why are people with this profile getting cancer? Cancer presents in a very unique way to each individual and often the answers to this question are not revealed until the person begins their journey of healing.

Once I became engaged in the right kind of care I needed, I had some perspective on just how much I expected of myself to keep going. I don't think I'm the only one who pushes myself in this world. Overextending and going to the end even if I'm crawling to make it over some imaginary finish line is part of these societal unspoken common agreements.

Where did these silent agreements come from, how did they get embedded in me?

All good questions. All I know is that I needed to unplug from them now in order to get well and stay unplugged after I am well.

Learning how to truly honor my body's wisdom is a lifelong path. I will never stop learning how to listen and take direction from the wisdom of my body!

This is my story and how I've learned to accept and love myself through all the challenges that life has offered me.

Five years have eclipsed since that fateful day in August 2016, which was also the day of my 25th wedding anniversary. I have now started to mark that day as an anniversary of "How lucky I am to be alive!"

Being alive trumps everything. Without my health, nothing else would matter.

I started journaling as a way to process what I was going through. I shared some of this writing on my blog and as I wrote friends told me how much my writing was helping them find strength in their own health struggles whether it was cancer or something else. This was a side benefit for me that had never entered my mind. I felt comforted that in all my suffering and enduring, I was somehow being of help to others in their own lives.

Having already spent over twenty-five years working as a holistic counselor, this was right in line with what I value most: sharing in meaningful and deep ways the synthesized practices I was discovering with others whose lives could be improved, extended, or even saved by them. This path has led me to the soul-nourishing work I now enjoy as a life coach, helping those who aspire to connect and live from a more authentic expression of their heart in order to embody more peace, love, and meaningfulness in their lives.

It's clear to me that I have to get out of my own way, believe that what I will be sharing with you about my healing journey with cancer will in its own way, uplift your spirit and together make us all stronger, give us more hope and the unwavering belief that at the end of the day, the body knows how to heal. My body knows how it needs to heal, and so does yours.

Nobody knows you better than you do. When you find yourself sitting across the desk with a medical specialist, never give up your power to them. Listen and then ask yourself, does what I'm hearing resonate with my heart and deep belief in my own power to heal? Will this support me in a way I can get behind 100%?

I want my healing journey with cancer to be an open book for you to benefit from and to find strength, purpose, and a great love of life as you make your own journey of healing back to wholeness.

This book is intended to guide and add to your treatment choices, not to replace any therapies you are doing; to give you more synergistic power for harnessing the energy that western allopathic and complementary medicines, along with lifestyle choices can provide for holistic healing.

I've included valuable soul-activating exercises from my **online course, Choose Life!**[1], including my **free template** to create your own **Integrated Lifestyle Healing Plan**[2] to help you dive more deeply into your own hero or heroine's journey. Be sure to find time to explore them as they will support your continuing transformation.

Bless you and your healing path.

CONNECT

What are your cancer questions?
In this book I share my journey and what I have learned
along the way. That being said, each of our experiences are
completely unique. Let me support you where you are.

Email me any questions, it would be my honor to hear from
you. Send them to: leslieapeake@gmail.com

PART I
SOUL EVOLUTION

UNRAVELING: FALLING INTO SURRENDER

 "Travelers, there is no path, paths are made by walking."

— ANTONIO MACHADO

Surrender was the biggest hurdle I had to face, even before trust and faith, was this deep, deep place of just letting it all go, surrendering. So much of life is about building up, holding on, and then controlling what we've created.

When I was diagnosed with colorectal cancer and numerous metastases that had implanted into both of my lungs, it never crossed my mind that five years later, I would still be on this journey.

Looking back now, I believe the biggest thing I've learned is how to surrender into the unknown and boldly take tiny steps forward. From surrender, I have spilled into trust, a deeper connection with faith/spirit, and loving myself and others.

Early in my journey, I unearthed assumptions I had always lived with:

- I should know what I'm doing.
- I should know where I'm going.
- I should have a plan.

Before my diagnosis, I didn't wake up in the morning wondering if I was going to live or die today. I took my ongoing life for granted. Now every day felt like a miracle that I had another opportunity to give everything I had to the day ahead and yet it was also confusing because I truly didn't know the outcome of my life.

One day my friend asked me very earnestly, "What is your plan?"

I looked at her with big open eyes, paused and felt a little ashamed when I replied, "I honestly don't know."

I knew there was no point in making up something just to appear that I had things under control.

I had to begin to practice welcoming all sorts of uncertainties and uncomfortable feelings. I had to live in a place of unknowing. Despite the discomfort I felt at first, I soon realized that this is part of being in the flow of life and we do not always have the answers.

I came to understand that although we may not know what the future holds, we have awareness of the moment, of how we feel, what we are thinking, the ability to make choices by listening to the immediate sensory information we are receiving in our body, mind, and heart. We have an awareness of the present energy based on the here and now.

Embracing the awareness of the moment requires learning to listen with a different ear.

To have trust in a different voice than the one that has become the loudest over the years. To make choices that are congruent with the energy felt in the heart and that support a path lived with connection to what one finds meaningful and purposeful.

Some may call this a greater purpose. **A Divine Purpose.**

One day while meditating I saw a huge banner across the inside of my head with capital letters that read: EVOLVING. The image was so large and bright that I couldn't miss it.

At this moment, I realized this is what I was doing amidst all of the treatments and changes going on in my life. I was evolving into a different person. This is when I began to connect what was happening to me in a much greater spiritual sense with how my physical world was rapidly disassembling itself.

I embraced the need to keep evolving as if in a spiraling process. Going inward at each turn and listening for what to do next.

As I committed to this constant evolution, I found myself questioning all aspects of my life. As I faced one part of my life and it resolved to a degree, another area would come up. This happened time and time again. It was as if all the non-essential pieces of my life were being released.

Usually, there was a lot of emotional baggage connected to this process. The emotions and attachments seemed to require more time for me to let them go on the physical level. I felt in the energetic layers of my being I was letting them go or changing the pattern, yet for the changes to be seen in my physical world, it took longer. It was like packing and repacking my suitcase for a long trip questioning what are the essential items I need and removing everything else that was extra and in essence weighing me down.

TRUSTING

I was written off work at 100% for at least six months, which felt like a shockingly long time to be away from my job as a school counselor. I soon accepted that my body needed my attention more than anything right now and I had to let go of work entirely in order to focus all my energy on the upcoming treatments.

I found myself at home in the mornings with an open agenda. Instead of hurrying to get ready for work, I wondered: what should I do? My deeply ingrained work schedule was removed and I was left with a feeling of unfamiliarity. I didn't need to rush from one task to the next anymore. None of this old way of living fit for me anymore.

Slowly, my life took on a natural reorganization of its own, influenced by chemotherapy appointments and complementary treatments I had booked during the week. In an attempt to not fill the empty moments with something, I stepped back and chose a place of stillness and non-action. I tried to get out of my head swirling with thoughts and just breathe, feel my heartbeat, sink into the vortex of heart energy in the fourth chakra and feel the pure loving power that resides there.

Then, as I sent energy down from my heart center through my legs and feet deep into Mother Earth, I took up the energy of the Earth through my whole body towards the heavens and allowed my whole Being to be held between the creative tension of Heaven and Earth. Then slowly, I began to take one step at a time.

What was it that I was holding onto so tightly and wanting to control? I had been unconsciously holding onto something for so long—my whole life—that when it came time to let go of, well, everything my life stood for at that moment... I wasn't sure what or why I had been holding on so tightly all these years.

Was it an idea or a value I had decided on as I grew up? Was it the idea of being the perfect mother, wife, employee, the perfect someone to all?

Questions surged forth, one after another. I found myself facing the fact that my body was rejecting my current lifestyle and choices. I knew I *had* to pay attention... or I was literally going to die.

As I searched for answers to these questions, it became clear to me that the psychological side of illness uncovers itself as a very different energy compared with how the physical breakdowns make themselves known. As the body's critical needs are taken care of, the balance tips from the physical to the multiple layers that make up the complex inner world.

Surrendering was then something I did unconsciously as a way to keep living. A part of me knew this was absolutely necessary and that in order to follow the next steps of what this meant, to surrender, I was going to have to be all-in for the journey ahead.

The way I had been living my life was providing basic comforts; food, shelter, family. I had been willing to sacrifice the bigger unknown adventure of my life for this.

This is not to say I was entirely unhappy. I focused on the areas where I found happiness, such as getting into the outdoors for biking, hiking, or skiing, planning trips over upcoming holidays, and socializing with friends, and left alone the parts that were not fulfilling me.

I realized the common theme among those things that felt lacking or absent of meaning was connection. How fulfilling were the connections I had with others? This spread through all areas of my life. Did I have meaningful and heartfelt connections in my life, and more importantly was I willing to look at how connected I felt to my own life?

I've come to realize that living half a life is not healthy, let alone deeply fulfilling.

When challenged with the call to venture into unknown territory by way of a surprise, potentially terminal illness, I sat up. I answered back with a "YES, I am ready to take on the challenge!"

HOW TO NOT LOOK BACK

I didn't know it at the time, but this kind of a challenge meant burning all the life rafts, allowing for no handy quick exit back into old habits and patterns where I had previously felt safe and secure.

As I continued on my journey, I discovered how prolonged illness strips away at the layers I had so carefully crafted together over time.

My energy became more focused on my body and needed a lot more time to rest in a peaceful, quiet room. I had to let go of being able to socialize with friends and go out to small gatherings. I began to notice how much I liked these get-togethers, as I felt like I belonged to a group of people that were outside of work. When this started to become less frequent, I had to find other meaningful ways to connect with friends.

Work can easily allow for short, focused conversations and leave you feeling like you're connected to a larger group beyond your family. This gives a nice social boost of belonging. When work falls away, so do these spontaneous conversations and feelings of inclusion.

A lengthy illness keeps you away from work, and the longer you're away, the fear is that you will be replaced and forgotten. Who are you now, without that safety and security of all the social connections made at work? Without being fully aware of what was happening I realized I asked myself were these connections essential to the central core of my Being?

I had to start looking elsewhere for connection, a sense of belonging, and meaningfulness.

I found myself in the realm of the soul, in which a different language presides, one that comes with no immediate answers, making for a challenging transition.

Here in this soft space awaits an invitation to make a passage through the door of the heart. A door that has always been there, waiting to be unlocked.

I cautiously unlocked this door with the key of my awareness. Before me lies an open field of space. Here is where I found myself learning how to navigate through confusion, uncertainty, and unpredictability. I was looking for a way through, but I saw no tracks. I fell to my logical thinking that knows what to do with a clearly laid out map, yet I found my heart immersed in a different kind of navigation system; one that relies on the sweet language of love and forgiveness.

With Cancer, or, I imagine, with any serious illness, the invitation to open your Heart Door or Cross The Threshold arrives and you have a choice; to remain as you have always lived or to turn towards the unknown and step into something new and uncertain.

I opened the door and found this hidden world is not as black and bleak as it appears from above. Venturing in with an open, non-judgmental awareness, the dark areas are responsive when met with a sense of curiosity, kindness, and love.

With a willingness to allow the body to feel into the 'broken places', there is a softening and vulnerability that begins to open up. And as the warmth of the Spring sun melts the ice in a river, love begins to flow into the areas where deep healing is needed.

. . .

What are the skills needed to wander this landscape once passed through the heart door?

One of the first skills I developed was to let go of the pieces of my life that no longer served me. I had images of laying these pieces onto a massive, long stone table that could withstand any heat.

Old resentments, grudges, anything my mind was holding onto with emotions of anger, frustration, or sadness showed up in my awareness like scenes across a movie screen and I knew they were not essential to my newly evolving Being. I visualized all these emotions, mental patterns, and habits that were built to support these resentments and grudges were immediately placed onto a stone table where a fire burned beneath it. I felt them burn up—a metaphorical burning that was held in the loving hands of surrender.

Whatever did not support my healing and a new way of being in my life was burned and had to be transformed. This applied to my work, all my relationships including my marriage, where I lived, the food I ate, and the beliefs I carried.

I was META-MORPHING. Witnessing myself going between finding shelter in the cocoon of my bedroom and burning up my life on the stone table. Slowly, I was morphing into a new person and a new way of being in the world.

All of this took enormous TRUST & COURAGE. I was ripped open and vulnerable in a way I had never known before. I was at the mercy, in the hands of a much greater force of life. A Universal flow now was taking over. I knew if I was to go on surviving this shit storm my body was going through, I had to look elsewhere and take a different path than I had been doing my whole life.

Cancer has the ability to open this door to another voice; to offer you the key to the heart door.

Does curiosity turn you towards this door, or simply a feeling of *"I've got nothing to lose"*?

However this door is offered to you, the important part is accepting the invitation.

Once you pass through, your descent into the underground begins: a surprising, tortuous journey that leads you to the doorstep of the Dark Night of the Soul.

For some, that translates as the big lesson the illness has brought you. Usually, this has a transformative effect on a major part of who you are, calling up for changes where there may have been misaligned energy or something that you've been holding back on sharing out of fear, or an aspect of yourself you have always been afraid to face.

Never having experienced this kind of "Dark Night" before, I thought one encounter with it would be enough. I thought I had met my Dark Night of the Soul a few months back after some enduring times with radiation, and was happy to have those experiences behind me.

Thinking that life would flow a little more easily now with Remission a part of my health status, I find this is not necessarily part of Life's Grand Plan.

The perspective that I have now allows me to see that early on, my thinking and timeline were way off. My oncologist would tell me in the early days, "This is not a sprint, Leslie. Think of it more in terms of a marathon."

But really, I had no idea what it truly meant to be in a marathon.

Slow, steady, turtle-like, with unwavering focus and determination. Thinking of the treatments, recoveries, and changes that my body would adapt to allowed me to relax in my mind about wanting this illness to hurry up and just go away.

This wasn't how it worked. There were no quick fixes, so I continued to keep accepting this as I could see that it took time for my body to adjust, heal, and keep going through what I was asking of it.

Remission is one of the big stepping stones, but it's not the end. Many more stones lay ahead. If they had names, they'd be called: Release, Renewal, Regenerate, Rebirth. I sense that there are more, but these are the ones showing up now.

LETTING GO

The world is a dense place, and so is the body. I've learned that if I can change the patterns created in the bodies that exist outside of my physical body, then this will shift what happens at the physical level. For me, this takes trust and patience. I also had support for this to happen as well.

As I went through the early treatments—six months of chemotherapy, two lung surgeries four weeks apart, hyperthermia, and craniosacral bodywork—I felt like I was on a rollercoaster of adrenaline. Everything was completely new to me and I was eager to experience what these therapies had to offer. Each type of treatment had different silver linings, and while some were harder to find than others, I was determined to grow from each one.

The lung surgeries were overall the most challenging for me, as I had never been operated on before and had no idea what to expect going in. I was excited in a way, because it meant that I would be getting rid of quite a few metastases that had spread to my lungs.

However, when I woke up in the intensive care unit after the surgery, I thought I was going to die there. I couldn't believe how my body felt, and I was freaked out.

All I could think was: *"I feel like my body has been run over by a dump truck."*

I couldn't move or do one thing for myself for days. The nurses were my lifeline, and without their compassionate, caring help tending to my every need, I would not have made it.

Miraculously, my body began to gain some strength. Slowly, I went from having zero energy to being able to move a bit and enjoy eating some food.

Were my heart and spirit big enough to embrace the biggest challenges that lay before me? I had to surrender and be willing to receive care, support, and love from others.

From the first lung surgeries, I learned that I needed a lot of support from others to get through my various recoveries. These recoveries called on every inner resource of self-compassion, resiliency, and maintaining a calm mind. I needed many people to lean on and surrender into their helping hands and hearts.

I began to feel that I was being held in a bigger circle of love by so many people and this love was opening me up in a way that felt different from what I'd experienced before. And this was just the beginning!

This energy of love was unconditional, it had no judgments or expectations. It just flowed. I started to notice it and open up more to it. For a person who had been helping others their whole life, it was now time to let go of helping others and open up to how it felt to be helped.

FORGIVENESS

Forgiveness surfaced as another path for letting life be as it is, without judgments or criticisms. A way of being where being yourself was enough. Not wasting energy on being resentful, angry, or holding a grudge against someone. Forgiving myself for not being perfect, not being enough. Letting my body be as it is, in a messed-up, broken state in need of massive attention, and finding a way to truly and deeply love it.

·   ·   ·

These are the parts that make up the container for my soul to evolve. I was wrapped up in these qualities and **energies of love, forgiveness, trust, compassion, surrendering, and gratitude** as I forged my way forward through the unknown territory that lay ahead. These qualities were my bright stars flickering in the clear, night sky.

SOUL ACTIVATION EXERCISE 1: CUTTING THE CORD

Now it's your turn to let go of what isn't serving you in your life with this powerful cord-cutting visualization. I suggest you read through the whole exercise first so you understand the purpose of what you're being called to do.

By reading through the exercise, you will have a feeling if this is the right time for you to try this or not. There is no pressure to do it. The exercise is simply an invitation to try something that's maybe new for you and can add to your personal journey of healing.

I am also including a link to an audio-guided visualization *lesliepeake.com/healingbonuses* that can make it easier for you to relax, close your eyes, and follow my voice without having to remember all the steps.

I encourage you to approach all of the exercises in the book with a sense of curiosity and an open mind and heart.

Whatever you need at this time will appear for you. Trust the process, and see what is revealed.

NOTE: Please read the explanation first, then perform the exercise.

Now it's your turn to activate your inner powers of healing with this first soul activation exercise.

The purpose of this exercise is to notice the areas in your body where emotional energy is leaking away from you and to call it back in order to use all of your energy for healing and strengthening your overall physical systems.

Cord-cutting is a technique that helps you to forgive yourself and others and set free the emotional chains that have been holding you down. Once the cord is cut, you may feel that it is possible to settle more deeply into your heart as a safe place to be, now that there is no more emotional turmoil pulling on your subconscious.

When you are holding a grudge, feeling resentful of someone, or holding onto anger, then you are essentially giving away your energy to this unresolved situation. Now is the time to release all of these non-essential aspects of your life, and reclaim this energy back into your system. You need this precious energy, now more than ever, for your healing.

Once you get settled you are going to ask your heart:

"What aspects of my life are not serving my greatest healing at this time?"

A person may appear, a way of thinking that holds you back may show up, an aspect of work or something about how you are living your life may come to your awareness.

Whatever it is, accept it without judgment and ask to be shown either a particular person or specific aspect of something in your life so that you are clear about who or what you are cutting the cord with.

Now that you know what is being asked of you, read ahead through this next part of the visualization and then close your eyes and go back through it in your own time.

Alternatively, you can go to *lesliepeake.com/healingbonuses* and listen to the recording of my voice taking you through the exercise.

Now, please find a quiet place and allow for no distractions or interruptions for the next 15-30 minutes. There is no specific amount of time for this exercise, this is just a guideline. Follow your rhythm and take the time you need.

VISUALIZATION:

Relax into a comfortable position in a chair, on the sofa, or in bed. Make sure your body feels supported with pillows, is warm enough, and you can begin to relax and focus on your breathing.

Close your eyes and bring your awareness to your inhalation as the air moves in through your nostrils and the exhalation of air going out through your nostrils. If breathing in and out through your nose is uncomfortable then try breathing in through your nose and out through your mouth.

Take at least 6 rounds of breathing in and out, slowing down your breathing and letting any thoughts drift out, feeling your body relax more and more.

When you are in a relaxed rhythm of breathing, ask yourself, "What parts of my life are not serving my greatest healing at this time?"

Continue to breathe, keep your mind empty, and wait for something to show up. It can be anything. At first it might not make sense to you. Stay free of judgment and just observe what comes to your awareness. It may be a memory, an emotion, a person, a belief you've been holding onto. Maybe there is more than one event that shows up. It's all OK.

Without thinking, choose the first thing that is highlighted for you and imagine a cord or string that is connected from you to this person, mindset, or memory. Notice what emotions come up, and imagine you can see this emotion connecting you to it. Let yourself imagine what the cord is made out of, the color, and any other qualities.

Really see and feel how it is connected to you and to whatever you've decided is not serving you anymore.

Now, when you're ready, take a deep breath in and on the exhale, imagine taking a pair of scissors or whatever is required to cut this cord. ON THE EXHALE, CUT IT AND SAY, "I SET YOU FREE."

Breathe out fully and completely letting this cord connection be severed forever and freeing yourself of all non-essential energy and ways of being that no longer serve your highest purpose.

Notice how you feel now as you continue to deeply breathe in and out.

Feel whatever new emotions have surfaced. Maybe these are feelings of freedom, forgiveness, gratitude, love, peace, and appreciation. These feelings are elevated emotions and live in the realm of your soul. Allow yourself to imagine and feel how the energy is flowing through your whole body.

Cord-cutting allows you to take back these lost areas of your life where energy has been leaking out of you and reclaim the energy back only this time with love and forgiveness.

It also allows you to send love and forgiveness to anyone involved, and set them free as well. Emotional energy is now freed up that settles you into a greater state of wholeness and healing.

Stay in this place for as long as you like.

When you feel ready, naturally open your eyes and gently come back into the space you are in staying connected to the newly elevated energy moving through your whole body.

Moving forward: Notice how you feel towards the person, situation, and/or energy you released. Observe your interactions and communication, and notice if the quality is different from how you experienced it before. What stands out for you? How can you release them even more thoroughly?

Go deeper: Continue your healing journey in my online course, Choose Life!

SOUL EVOLUTION IN 7 PARTS

THE HIDDEN GIFTS OF EVOLVING

I didn't know what I was doing, I simply kept following the energy.

I listened inwardly all the time for feedback and messages I was receiving from my body, my mind, in my meditations and daily life. A message could flicker into my awareness at any time. Sometimes in the shower, taking a walk, cooking, writing, the feedback was constant and I had a commitment to myself to listen openly and respond in ways that supported healing in my body and in every aspect of my life.

This was a new way of making choices that were immediate and in alignment with my desire to continue living. Shifts came first internally, then externally, slowly transforming my world.

Cancer was showing me how to save my life, and not be afraid of evolving into the person who was emerging inside me. All I had to do was keep saying, "yes" to every experience and challenge that was presented to me.

One of the first practical things I said yes to was choosing to get a port-a-cath (medical port) put in, which would replace having to get needles all the time. I knew getting a needle in my arm was stressful and something I really didn't like, so when the suggestion of having a port put in was presented to me, I immediately said yes. This was actually my first little surgery, and I jumped on it with welcoming arms. It also meant I could begin the chemotherapy treatments immediately afterward.

Saying yes to what kept showing up in my awareness has not always been easy, as it's completely reshaped the way I view myself, affecting my work, relationships, and how I choose to use my energy.

Tucked away within the interwoven layers of hidden gifts that have been revealed to me lies a wealth of richness clothed in unconditional love, compassion, and forgiveness.

I discovered that, in order to continue evolving and remaining true to a bigger, universal flow of energy, I had to keep coming back to 7 different aspects of my evolution: taking my power back, developing presence, breathing, awareness & interruption of my "auto-pilot," energy, recovery, and hanging on and letting go.

ONE: TAKING YOUR POWER BACK ~ OPENING UP WHAT'S BEEN LOCKED AWAY

I want you to know that if you are faced with a life-threatening diagnosis, whether it's cancer or any other kind of illness, it's a wake up call. It's a sign that there's something you need to listen to right now and that your life is somehow out of balance. Your challenge is going to be finding a way into a new level of balancing, a fluidity that flows and is ever-changing.

You are the one who knows where the imbalance is, and what you need to do.

That is both the good news and the bad news: that deep in your heart, you have the answers, and it's time to listen to them and make choices.

I know you're going to want other people to tell you the answers and show you the way. "Here's what to do: take steps 1, 2, 3, and all will be well." Maybe this approach can work sometimes, for a while.

However, if you want to experience a transformation within your whole being, now is the time to ask yourself, "What have I not been listening to that I've been trying to tell myself for a while now?"

This was my big challenge, because I didn't start here.

I had warnings. I know I did, because I could flip back through these pictures in my mind, different choice points along the journey of my life. I had a pattern of putting up with things that I didn't like by not speaking up and sharing how I was feeling and what I was thinking. My tendency was to stuff this energy inside and close the lid on it, pretending that I could manage and was strong enough to carry on.

At the time, I found my workplace gave me plenty of opportunities to overcome this challenge. I realized that I shared in groups where I felt safe and respected. However, I didn't expand this to more challenging circumstances where I felt unsafe.

I would reflect back on how I was making my choices: was it out of fear, or out of a trust and a zest for life to follow a deeper passion? What was I choosing?

Whatever I chose to do at that time was with the inner resources I had, and what felt right to me.

Looking back, I can see that some of these choices were made out of fear. Fear of not being able to make it in the world and be respected, of not knowing what my purpose was, of not having job security and a roof over my head. I made choices that overall felt safe, yet still gave me some satisfaction and happiness in life.

I can look back and see the sacrifices I made at a soul level.

What I want to tell you right now is that, in a strange way, the universe has given you a gift. "**Here you go: you have another opportunity. You get to decide what that opportunity or opportunities are going to be, and how you're going to use them.**"

There's going to be a lot of other voices in the ring with you, and that's normal. You're going to have to decide which voices you're going to listen to, and which ones you're going to say goodbye to.

These voices will be from family, spouse or partner, children, friends, doctors, specialists, caregivers, lots of different people. There will be other voices unique to your experiences that come up. You will recognize them. They will be based on fear and trying in their own way to protect you and keep you safe in a way you've always known. There will be new voices now saying, "Maybe I'm ready to try a different way."

It's time to trust in a new way, even though you don't know where it's going.

This brings me to how uncertain life can be. Living in a world that is safe and protected, knowing what's going to happen every day keeps you within your comfort zone. You can feel happy and content here.

There's nothing wrong with this, until you're faced with an illness. Then it's time to look at these areas that you have kept safely controlled. Maybe they're tucked in a box and you don't want to open up that lid because everything you've kept neatly packed up will come flying out. The thought of this happening can be incredibly frightening and scary.

It's at these choice points that my inner discipline is tested, having to just watch as this hurricane of thoughts comes sweeping through the window of my awareness. To be willing to acknowledge they are there is scary enough. Holding strong to let the force of them keep passing through is a real test of mindful presence, of detachment, of awareness without judgment.

However, keeping the lid on comes with some big costs at a soul level. And with an illness, you don't have the luxury of keeping the lid on anymore.

It's time to open up.

And that's exactly what I did. I took the lid off my life, and said, "Show me what I need to do, what needs to change and how to let go of the things that are not working."

However you decide to move forward, whether it's through conventional medicine, complementary or healing energy medicine, implementing lifestyle changes or a combination of all of these, called integrative medicine, you are going to have to put a lot of care and attention on building up this energy of openness in your body.

TWO: DEVELOPING PRESENCE ~ COMMITTING TO YOUR LIFE AND WHAT IS

I have been lucky or maybe guided by some greater force that has connected me to health care doctors and body/mind therapists who I consider quite amazing in their field. When I found out I had cancer, I automatically attracted the specialists I needed in my life to help me on this journey. People with whom I would be able to be myself entirely, and whom I could trust with my life.

It's clear to me that healing from cancer, or any disease, is not just contained to the physical body, but very much a discovery of the self in the mental, emotional, and spiritual aspects as well. Healing into wholeness takes time. It's intricate, messy, confusing, and complicated.

While the body needs so much love, care, and attention to right itself back on a cellular level, the mind needs help to deal with all of the new thoughts it's producing and the emotions that are now being felt.

Not to mention, one wonders: *What does all this mean on a spiritual level? How can I accelerate healing on each level?*

All of these aspects of my being show up loud and clear, moving in and amongst the others presenting themselves in a jumbled order while sitting in front of the oncologist, the house doctor, the naturopathic doctor, or the mind-body healing therapist. Talking is always a component of the relationship, but there is also an energetic, non-verbal component that happens between the practitioner and the patient. I ask myself: *"What kind of relationship nurtures the healing factor to have the greatest potential?"*

This was my focus, without knowing any specific answers. I just knew that I needed to feel connected in a non-verbal way, a heartfelt way, with whomever I worked. Regardless, of the fact that I didn't already know anyone to work with, I wanted a connection, a bond, and a commitment that went beyond words. An energy that would be nourished not dependent on time or shared experiences.

I find myself thinking about what is too personal in a helping therapeutic relationship?

At University, I learned about transference and not allowing my emotions or the patient/client's to get transferred into the professional relationship. However, when I think about this concept, there is something in it that already sets up a boundary in me, closing a part of myself off.

How can deep healing have a chance when I've already created a separation?

While I have always held the space for connection and openness in working with others when I have been the "helper," I am now experiencing a different side of this being on the receiving end of care. I'm feeling how much more of a vastness of open space there can be for connection, a deep pool of compassion and unconditional loving, one that is not finite, but everflowing.

I am experiencing that it is possible to cultivate a genuine friendship in this practitioner–patient relationship, and above all else, cultivating a sense of trust and a deep connection that has its roots in healing.

"What friendship means has much to do with our willingness to relate openly and directly with people and situations just as they are." Saki Santorelli talks about all of us perhaps wishing to be related to in this manner; that we can just be open and frank about whatever it is that's going on whether it's tough or pleasant.

To me, this is the blessing of working with someone knowing I can show up and just be however I am in that moment. To simply be present without thinking or worrying

I need to be somehow different and that my views are respected and considered in the overall healing journey.

When going through chemo treatments, it can be a mixed bag of how I respond from week to week, and there's nothing more welcoming than having my Oncologist be an active and interested listener in how I'm feeling.

What was it that I looked so forward to each week when I met with my Oncologist? My immediate response is his handshake. When he extends his hand, his handshake is packed with energy, warmth, hope, commitment, and compassion. Our conversation that follows just backs up all of these feelings.

Santorelli explores what the practitioner-patient relationship embodies and states, "It is possible that the entire healing relationship is actually founded on friendship." I know for myself when counting on someone for their knowledge, wisdom, and expertise, friendship is fundamental to the healing process.

I didn't expect to have such profound connections with the main specialists I saw every week, people who at first were total strangers. These same people who graciously extended their hand and heart out to me inviting me to step into this unknown territory with them. This was a compassionate invitation that says, "You are not alone, and I know you are suffering."

I had been practicing mindfulness meditation for a few years already, but then I began to incorporate loving kindness and compassion practices into my meditation. These daily practices have helped me learn how to treat myself with kindness, care, and to offer myself the possibility of feeling safe, living with ease and a sense of peacefulness. I know that cultivating these qualities within myself have helped me to be more open to people who were not that long ago strangers to me and are now people that I care about and feel safe with.

The line between practitioner and patient becomes blurred and is "not defined by role, knowledge, education, or status." There is an equality about the relationship as Santorelli points out. It is an exploration that asks for a commitment to openness and a willingness to be present with each other regardless of what presents itself.

Mindfulness asks us to be awake in the moment, to be non-judgemental, and to acknowledge what is. These states of being are the basis for an intimate friendship that can carry one through the toughest of times.

THREE: BREATHING ~ LEARNING TO USE YOUR BREATH AS A HEALING TOOL

Can you remember a time when you were so caught up in your thoughts that you didn't pay attention to the ache in your stomach or the tightness in your shoulders?

It's normal to have days when you're just feeling separated or detached, when the connection between what's going on in your mind, and what your body is trying to tell you, is harder to sense. This feeling of mind-body disconnection can also have ripple effects, sometimes felt as a sense of loneliness or not belonging.

· · ·

No one said this was easy. The most challenging time to be present is in these moments of intense swirling thoughts, to keep breathing and at the same time experience a sense of being a witness to the whole process.

Let's deal with the body first, because now things have become so bad that they've manifested in the physical and you're essentially in the emergency room, so it's triage time. The most urgent needs get immediate attention, and if you've got a life-threatening illness, that's probably going to have to do with your body.

Breathing, letting energy and compressed emotions out through tears and asking, *"What do I need right now to bring self-compassion to my Being? I know this is a moment of suffering... and I am not alone."* Leaning into all of your inner resources and using them.

The question is, what's your go-to formula for finding that harmonious sweet spot where you feel at peace, connected with yourself, others, and the world, where the energy is flowing, and you feel happy inside just because?

For myself, movement is my breath of life.

Dancing and moving my body go hand in hand with breathing and have always been the pathway towards my heart opening up to more happiness in life.

Ever since I was a young girl, I have danced. I felt joyful and free dancing. My mind became quiet and any thinking effortlessly dissolved during these dance sessions. These early experiences I stumbled upon have carried me through the decades of my life showing me what it means to have a unified mind and body.

As dancing gave way to other forms of contemplative movement such as authentic movement simply meaning moving with no agenda other than to follow the whispers of energy that I felt within and to give them a voice of expression.

Through this exploration, I could feel the borders between my mind and body dissolving. A quiet, empty mind and an awake body allowed for all the sensations and emotions inside to be accepted as they were.

Breath naturally supports movement and the heart generously opens as the whole body feels more connected and safe.

When you turn your attention towards your breathing, you naturally open up the channels of awareness. Your nervous system begins to slow down, your mind becomes quiet, and your heart begins to soften and relax. Energy flows. When energy flows, healing happens. Your body has an opportunity to reset and renew itself, both physiologically and psychologically.

This is an exquisite place to be hanging out in. A place where there is no rushing to get somewhere or get one more thing done. No, this moment, this space is simply full and bursting with joy, love, happiness, and the fullness of the present moment.

Who wouldn't want to experience more of these positive, life-enriching feelings?

Through a series of unforeseen events, I was fortunately introduced to Qigong. First, when I was living in Shanghai, China. I must admit, I took for granted the amazing Wushu-trained teachers I had at that time. I immediately took to the slow and deep meditative movements they were teaching me. My body now had an impression of Qigong that would be with me forever.

It wasn't until I was in the middle of recovering from cancer treatments that Qigong was re-introduced to me. My body took to it like bees to flowers. I couldn't get enough and I was so grateful to be guided back to movements that I could do again.

Even with reduced mobility and energy levels, I was able to connect again with a meditative movement that became my breath of life. I knew in my bones, my blood, and my heart that Qigong was helping to restore my whole body back to health and opening me up to a larger source of healing energy.

FOUR: AWARENESS OF YOUR AUTOPILOT & INTERRUPTING IT

For a long time, I struggled to keep my daily routines running.

I felt weak inside. I didn't have the vibrant, core energy I knew I could have and I didn't know where it had gone or how to get it back.

I knew I needed to do more self-care for myself and I increased the time I spent meditating and doing yoga in an attempt to find ways to unwind from my workday and release stress. It didn't feel like enough, though, and I wasn't sure how else to go about helping myself. It never entered my mind that I might be really sick, especially with something like cancer.

Abruptly, I was being pulled out of an autopilot controlled by a series of unconscious routines that dominated my day. I had no idea how deep this rut had become.

I realized how far away I had grown from honoring my intuition over the years. How did this happen? At one point in my early thirties, I was teaching women about how to open up to their intuition and make choices based on what was true for them, not others. I witnessed women creating businesses and changing their lives that reflected their passion and values. It was a wonderful time to be part of their lives and witness their transformations.

It's not as important to wonder where, when, did I get lost, but that I am reconnecting with this place inside myself that only I can know and act from.

A cancer diagnosis certainly made me stop and quickly begin to refocus everything about my life. It sharpened my mind to focus on healing, not allowing myself to go down the track of being a statistic or getting caught up in thinking this is too hard or why me.

"This isn't fair!"

Of course, I'm human, I have these thoughts and acknowledge them. I just make sure to move on. They're not thoughts I want to get stuck in. I know they eventually become destructive and turn inwards on my body, just at a time when I need my thoughts to really be supporting and working for me.

All those thoughts that were running on autopilot are now under closer scrutiny.

The question becomes: what kind of relationship do you want to have with all the automatic, autopilot thoughts?

When you turn toward them and commit to waking up from your unconscious habits, you become acutely aware of what kind of thoughts are going through your head and catching them and saying *"Stop,"* or *"No thanks; I don't want that thought anymore."*

This is where listening to your inner voice or intuition becomes everything. It has to be *your* voice, and no one else's. If you're used to listening to other people's voices about what you need to do, or being driven by a stream of constant "shoulds," the challenge now is to turn inward and listen honestly and closely to your voice. From this place, the wellspring of life can begin to flow.

Working to get better at catching the unhelpful inner chatter is a daily process. You begin to cultivate an attunement with this critical voice that can easily overtake the present moment and try to deaden your authentic voice in a misguided attempt to keep you "safe."

Sick is not safe. It's time to risk following your heart, wherever it may lead.

One of the things I hope you get from reading this book is that anything is possible for you when you open up your mind and soften your heart.

When you take the lid off your life and let everything come flying out, it lands in all kinds of crazy places, allowing for new possibilities you never even considered.

Yes, it will be uncertain, and it will feel uncomfortable. Yet at the same time, it will feel exhilarating, and you will feel like you can get through anything, whatever it is that you need to do. These feelings are so empowering and stop the autopilot track your body has been following.

Instead, you are telling yourself that you want to live, and you're going to do whatever it takes.

I'm always looking for the silver lining in difficult situations that life brings me. For me, there always have to be positive benefits if I have to go through something tough. I look for the learning, the goodness that's being brought to me from a hard place I have in my life. Cancer is certainly no exception to this and the continuous challenges it brings to me.

When doing some healing work, I was asked, "What is the first thing that comes to your mind when I ask you: What's been positive about having cancer?"

I closed my eyes, took a breath and immediately said, "Time to take care of myself."

When in my adult life have I felt justified just focusing on me and spending time wholeheartedly doing exactly what I feel I need to do everyday?

It's not that I haven't done things for myself since I took on the many varied roles a woman does in our modern, busy world. That's the paradox and part of what confused me about being told I had cancer. I did things that I enjoyed, taking time to exercise, practice yoga, meditate, and get into the outdoors.

However, I realize now that partly it was the way I was going about it. I was unconsciously participating in these activities because I had a belief that they would grant me immunity against sickness, quietly guaranteeing that I would stay healthy, strong, and enjoy lots of mobility. I wasn't doing it just for the sake of enjoying the activity, and the happiness I felt while engaged. An unconscious, hidden agenda tainted these activities.

When your body develops an illness, especially an overtly life-threatening one, it becomes apparent that the deepest and most important relationship you're going to have is with your Self. No one will be able to tell you what you need to do except you.

As long as your body and soul are meant to be here, having an experience in this lifetime, you're going to be here. No one is free of the uncertainty of knowing when it's time to move on into the next transition.

However, you are here, right now, in this moment, dealing with whatever it is that's in front of you. That is: being alive, being fully in the moment, accepting and choosing how you want to move forward in the best possible way, with the best quality of life.

And this is a real gift, that your thinking has shifted from autopilot to awakening. Some of the thoughts you will notice that don't consume and override your day may be, *"What do I need to do next to finish my day, or what's still on my checklist?"* The constant nattering of thoughts that drown out any voice of listening to your heart for what needs to happen next instead.

With your awakening to your needs, you can pay attention to what is important for you to attend to. How do you want to increase the quality of your life and the way you make choices? Take the time to decide on how you want to support yourself and bring more loving energy into your life as you go through the next steps of whatever it is you're called upon to do.

This is a journey. A marathon, not a sprint. Relax and find your rhythm.

It's a courageous one, and you're writing it. That's the exciting and scary part. You get to write the journey of your life and direct how it goes. You can always create a different outcome, a different ending.

The choices I make when I tune in and listen to my intuition are the right choices for me. That's all that matters. The choices I make about how to heal my body become all part of how I transform my body-mind-spirit back to a vibrant state of being.

This is my personal treatment protocol, true to who I am. There is no one recipe. Each human being is a unique individual and this becomes the challenge.

Trust yourself enough to follow your inner guidance.

When you unhinge yourself from the numbing patterns of being on autopilot, you take on more personal responsibility for your life.

If you wonder, *"Am I doing it right, making the correct choices?"*, look for feedback. Are things falling into place that support you, are you feeling happy, content, satisfied? These are signs that say "yes" back to you.

I had a dream where I was the subject of an experiment. We were recording everything that was going on in my body and observing changes. There were two parts to the dream, one was about letting go and the other was about feeding and nurturing. Like a scale weighing out both processes and searching for a balance, or a homeostasis in the body. We were seeing how effectively everything was working, and what kind of progress there was.

Life is an experiment.

You don't know what you're doing all the time, and so you try different things to see what feels right, what works best, what provides the results you are looking for.

Now, this practice is my life and it has opened me up to so many wonderful exchanges with people and supported me to not be afraid to listen to my intuition again and again and then to make choices that place me in the center of my personal power.

FIVE: ENERGY ~ TAPPING INTO GREAT LOVE

One of the things I wanted to do was to disarm the fear of cancer for everybody, especially my kids. I didn't want cancer to be the elephant in the room, or something that I hid in a closet and locked the door on. Pretending it wasn't there, or that everything was fine and there was nothing to discuss, wasn't an option for me.

I wanted it out in the open, and to talk about it. I found myself naturally wanting to share my diagnosis with all my friends and colleagues. I knew that by doing so, it would help people process *their* fears so they could put their energy towards supporting my healing.

In this way, I could direct the narrative of how energy could flow and guide others in the process.

I quickly realized that the energies of worry, fear, and overwhelm only increased a sense of stress and tension in the body and didn't enhance or support healing. While these emotions are real and valid and need to be acknowledged, they have a contraction of energy around them.

By giving others an opening into my experiences and treatments, it was an invitation for them to process their own emotions that were coming up for them. This was an opportunity for us all to find our center in this untethering experience, and then, according to each person's willingness and ability, to send me elevated healing energy.

I was asking for the energy of joy and hope, love and faith, gratitude and healing.

As people were able to feel these elevated emotions and send this energy out to me, I felt more of it. This cycle of energy increased its power and we all became stronger as time moved along.

The path ahead just didn't seem so scary and ominous. Focusing in this way took away the power of a prognosis of what a stage four diagnosis can signify, and the horrible thoughts the mind can conjure up.

I know because my mind would naturally have worried thoughts when I would hear this kind of diagnosis for somebody else. Yet, when it was my life, affecting my body, it was very clear that I didn't want to sink into that kind of negative contraction.

Social connections became a container of this energy that was so potent and powerful, loving, supportive, and fearless. There was no room for fear yet there was all the space and openness to talk about whatever anybody wanted to talk about with me.

I found this approach disarmed fear. It neutralized the very difficult emotions that came up and gave them a place to be and then to dissolve. That dissolution flowed into a single-minded focus on healing. Healing with love that was sent for the highest good to be received as my body needed it, unconditionally. In all kinds of ways, people were also experiencing their own healing in their lives. This was the beauty and magic of our social connections, whether in-person or virtual.

While I was experiencing stronger energetic connections within virtual circles, I was fortunate to be able to cultivate meaningful connections with many of my healthcare specialists.

A healing relationship begins with a small kindling of friendship. Building this fire together is what keeps the friendship growing while developing a base of trust, openness, communication, and a feeling of warmth. Each visit I had with my complementary doctor was like adding a piece of wood to the fire for the flames to continue burning.

Heat is energy. This reminds me of my hyperthermia treatments I underwent in tandem with the chemo infusions, and I am instantly transported back to one of those visits.

The total treatment time was 3 hours, raising my core body temperature up to 38.9°C to induce and hang out in a fever state in order to create a cellular environment that cancer cells cannot thrive in, and then slowly lowering my temperature back down.

While lying there feeling extremely hot, it suddenly dawned on me, the logic behind allowing your child to go into a fever state instead of dampening the body's response to healing when they are sick. Allowing the fever to "break" on its own allows the body to deal with the toxic cells by killing them off. Of course, it's a fine line between making sure your child doesn't overheat for too long, and keeping them cooled off with a damp towel. I've been there with my kids when they were young, and it can be a tough call to know how long to hang out there with them before making a visit to the doctor.

For myself, it's about finding the level of heat I can tolerate and still remain safe in my body.

Being in a hyperthermia bed and raising your temperature is closely monitored with blood pressure, heart rate, intravenous minerals, and of course temperature. When I get into the bed and the walls are zipped up, my body lets go into a deep sigh of relief.

I like this place.

I'm back here again, and I prepare to sink into another world for a few hours. It really is another world. The body completely begins to relax, the mind starts to unwind and all the commentary running through begins to subside. The skin softens as it heats up and I imagine releasing toxins as my core temperature increases.

An image appears in my mind of all the blood vessels in my body, like small tributaries carrying out the old cancer cells and other toxic material being floated out by tiny water pathways of sweat. My mind does not easily relate to the chemistry and molecular biology that goes on in my body, so I naturally find other ways to imagine how cells can exit out of me.

I believe the imagery that comes to you is important to trust and roll with. I'm learning to accept my own imagery for how my body wants to talk to me without analyzing it. To let it flow, like the sweat flowing out of me as I lie in the bed, heating up.

Thoughts swirl in and out of my head, emotions move through my body, and in an instant, a flash of insight shoots through me where everything I've been thinking and feeling comes together with powerful clarity. Afraid that I might lose this moment, I call over to my doctor to come and be with me. It is in these unexpected times that we have the most unique exchanges.

Today, I talk about the Great Love that keeps recurring between myself and some of my health care specialists. I depend on these people to help guide me and be present to meet me in the difficult places I encounter. The ones who I see regularly, we practice together, dropping into this space beneath the words, letting go of the expectation to 'fix' the broken pieces, and the willingness to just be with what is happening now. These are the moments where this greater connection to healing begins to open up.

I call it a Great Love, an energy that goes beyond the limitations of the physical body and my identification with my Self as an individual separate from another human being.

Having opportunities every week to slow down and attune my mental focus into being open to the healing I can receive from the treatment, whether it is a chemo infusion, hyperthermia, energy healing, bodywork, or having an MRI or some other strange kind of exam; I am allowing for the possibility of connecting to a bigger energy field that exists beyond the walls of my body.

What do I discover in orienting my focus this way time and time again?

A regenerative, healing quality begins to flow through me, not bound by time or judgment. It is free of all constraints and comes in just as a pure loving energy.

Life offers me these opportunities to sit with another and share this field of love. I'm finding this is the ground, the foundational relationship between the practitioner-patient and between the people in my life where I share a meaningful relationship. This is where I feel healing happens. It is in the *being*, together. The moments where each of us can suspend the urge to *"just get the problem fixed so I can move back to the way life used to be."*

The wise practitioner and caregiver knows that life will never be the same for the person who is facing a health crisis and they are not trying to rush them back to their old life.

For that would be going backwards after so much work had been done to heal the call to crisis.

Over time, a new quality of life begins to emerge, a different way of moving through the world. It's important to remain open to the possibilities of what this new life offers.

When the Great Love energy is flowing, I am now realizing that there's nothing to do with it, just be with it. Let it in. Allow this divine loving energy to do the healing. It is purely a joyful, happy, detached energy flowing with freedom.

I drop into this river of energy and allow myself to be supported by the buoyancy of love. This is where I find my strength to live with ease and a deep sense of peace. Everything else I do is supported from this inner place of love that exists both within me and beyond.

I often have an image of myself as a tree, roots reaching deep into the Earth, branches and leaves extending up towards the Heavens. My tree was a Magnolia. With the warm weather and sunshine, the Magnolia flowers have all opened where I live. It's a wonderful reminder of the beauty and strength that lives within me, others, and nature.

Saki Santorelli reflects what I am struggling to find words to express:

When "we touch the brokenness and wholeness of being --- our humanity---with less struggle, more ownership, allowing ourselves to be more fully with what is" we arrive in the fullness of our entire universe.

This journey has become my school of life, my major diving into a deeper practice of mindful and compassionate meditation while turning towards wholeness and embodying a Greater Love. Meeting my life in this way offers a vast potential for integration and an opportunity for transformation.

Patiently and silently, the stillness of love waits for my heart to unfold.

SIX: RECOVERY ~ GETTING WHAT YOU NEED DURING RECOVERY PERIODS & HARD TIMES

Recovery comes in many forms, and after each intervention I've had, the body always has a different way of responding, even after the exact same intervention. I think I know how it will go and what I'll need, yet each time I'm surprised by what shows up.

Over these past years of many recoveries, I now have a memory bag filled with possibilities and various ways to support my mind and body. Even though I still fool myself into thinking I know how this will go and how I'll feel, I am constantly making adjustments as each day reveals new information.

Recovery is not only on the physical level. It can be just as intense on the mental and emotional levels as well. As my body was working hard to recover physically and needing an enormous amount of energy for this, I noticed other aspects of my life were calling for me as well.

My inner voice had turned up the volume and it was impossible for me to ignore it now. Different areas of my life were now demanding more attention from me as my body became stronger. A new dance was developing as my awareness was becoming more keenly attuned to the other parts of my life that were not working so well for me.

I remember talking to myself, saying, "Can't you just give me a break so I can relax for a while?"

The answer was, "No."

Everything in my life became part of my healing journey and was tied into my recoveries as I gained physical strength. Life began to accelerate.

For now, after a major intervention such as the radio-chemo treatments, I had to turn my full attention to my body and gently give myself all the support I could for this recovery. It was not only treating my hands and feet as the skin recovered, but also my pelvic floor and perineum from the burning side effects of the radiation.

After completing 6 weeks of Radio-Chemo treatments, I had 5 days to rest at home before boarding a plane to Canada to see family and friends. My body was still reeling from the intense side effects of the treatment and in fact they seemed to be increasing. The pads on my fingertips were continuing to crack and become more sensitive to touch and temperature, as were my feet.

I wasn't sure how I was going to navigate transport to the airport and actually get on the plane by myself? It wasn't until a friend said she was going to drive me to the airport and that I should call ahead for wheelchair assistance that I relaxed into thinking, "Maybe this is possible?"

I find it amazing that even in my desperate physical state, I still didn't think I could ask for help! Is it because, as women, as mothers, we are conditioned to just get the job done, regardless of how we feel?

Breaking this pattern of conditioning is so challenging.

I had to be told that I would receive help and there was no questioning it. Once I just opened up to receiving, I was able to relax about the travel that lay ahead. Being able to go through the Zürich airport in a wheelchair was really quite fun, especially when escorted by a kind man originally from Tibet.

The summer theme naturally took on an ebb and flow of the tides. From the West Coast of Canada to Norway's North of the Arctic Circle Coast. The weather angels were making sure there was plenty of sunshine and warm temperatures for me. Receiving so much sunshine and blue skies everyday was truly like a healing from the Heavens.

Slowly but surely, my body was able to have a full recovery. I felt like a snake shedding its skin, waiting for it to be replaced with baby soft finger pads and new soles for my feet.

As the skin and sensitivity on my feet toughened up, I was able to walk for longer periods and take myself along the sandy beaches of Jericho in Vancouver to the rocky coastline of the Gulf Islands, and eventually out to the vast expanse of white sand beaches around Tofino on Vancouver Island's West Coast.

I hadn't spent so much time by the ocean in a long while, and I realized how much I missed being at the water's edge, walking the empty beaches, staring out to sea, and breathing in the ocean air.

Stepping away from the continuous pulse of doctor's appointments and treatments and replacing it with an open agenda and the company of dear soul friends helped me to lose track of time, let my mind go and find a new rhythm. To forget about being sick. To just be. To feel healthy. To forget about tests and results. To enjoy the moment for what it is. So empowering and healing.

This was my summer break, and it was so worth it to slow life down on the treatment front. Friends thought our trip looked busy because we did so much, but in truth, each day unfolded according to how much energy I had, and with no need to rush or do anything specific. I found it easy to sink into the moments and be re-energized by not rushing around.

New ways of being bring about new levels of energy.

It wasn't until the week before my scheduled follow up exams were to happen that my mind began to turn towards doctors, clinic visits, tests, chemo, and the status of my body. I noticed thoughts creeping in with concern, nervousness, and the fact of facing another cycle of chemo infusions.

It's hard to avoid these kinds of thoughts.

I would acknowledge them, breathe into my feelings, and let them pass by. Not giving them too much attention. I wanted to keep enjoying the present moment; the stunning scenery of the Lofoten Islands, the sunshine, the hiking, and the lovely cafés.

Following 8 weeks after the radio-chemotherapy, I was scheduled to have control exams for lungs, liver, and my rectal area where the primary tumor had started. While these results would provide hopefully greater peace of mind, I noticed my body was becoming increasingly agitated about the exams. This year, I have had plenty of practice listening to the voice of my body and simultaneously listening to the thinking mind and its voice. The two are often not in sync. This is when I run into intra-mind-body static.

 If the ocean can calm itself, so can you. We are both salt water mixed with air.

The body is not rational. It does not get caught up in what it's supposed to do and how it should act, it simply feels and responds, at a cellular level. Can I be brave enough to listen to it and take a stand of respond-ability? That's my new word for responsibility, meaning: willing to respond in a way that honors the body's voice and choose actions that allow for this non-verbal expressiveness to be acknowledged and answered.

I have a choice when I notice the intra-mind-body static: to either bury the body voice because the mind says, "It's no big deal, just a follow up check," or allow it to speak?

Body words may express themselves in the form of muscle tightness or weakness, butterfly feeling in the stomach, shaky muscles, sounds, and/or tears. These are all valid and real ways that the body speaks.

This time, I allow tears to flow until the stream subsides and the water is calm. I can breathe freely again and find myself in a better mental and emotional state to meet the exams with a sense of ease and greater peace.

Just as the ocean tide ebbs and flows, so does the water that my body is made up of. Connect to the rhythm of the moon, and flow like the tide.

On the 14th of August, the mail started arriving again for me. Usually, it has to do with medical statements and bills, so I wasn't in any rush to open it up.

Later in the evening, though, I was feeling strong and positive, so I peeled back the sticky closure. To my surprise, I saw that it was the results from my rectal endosonography exam, the big "control" exam after the 8 weeks of radio-chemo treatments. These results show how well the treatments worked to eliminate all cancer cells in the primary tumor area.

As it's all in German, I could really only grasp the tone of the results by looking at the pictures and the final page. The pictures matched exactly my visualizations in this part of my body: reddish pink, shiny, smooth, healthy looking.

The final page: Klinische Angaben (Clinical Information) Status nach RCT (Status after exam). Rektumkarzinom: Remission (Rectal cancer: Remission).

One word we ALL understand, whether we know German or not is: REMISSION!!

My eyeballs popped out with the shock of finally seeing these words! I wasn't expecting it, even though I initially knew the tissue looked very healthy after the exam. Seeing the words on paper somehow gave it more real meaning.

What a massive sense of relief! I sank into moments of gratitude feeling like heaven had just granted me another period of grace. I was completely happy!

SEVEN: HANGING ON & LETTING GO

Within 24 hours of receiving that report on the status of the tumor as *Remission*, I was in for the first appointment with my oncologist to begin 4 more chemo infusions, one per week.

We went over the excellent news of the tumor and all cancer cells being completely gone, replaced with healthy tissue and new cells. I could now begin to use the past tense when referring to this tumor.

Oddly enough, that took some conscious thought. I hadn't realized I was on autopilot when talking about the tumor, always in the present tense.

Mindshifts around how I use language when speaking about my body and the cancer is important to recognize. It's easy to stay locked in a certain frame of reference and begin to over identify with cancer being ever present as a new identity.

I found out that the choice to do radio-chemo treatment (in place of the invasive operation that would have removed a large part of my bowel area and left me learning to navigate a new way of living with a stoma) is only cautiously offered as an option because there is not enough evidence yet to prove its safety and effectiveness.

At the time, all I heard was that there was an alternative to having a very invasive operation that would change my bowels and digestive process for life. I was not keen to offer my body up for any more surgical operations, having learned from experience that there was so much more to an operation in terms of the after-effects of recovery. I was much more cautious now, and willing to try any alternative to cutting me open.

There are 900 cases my oncologist is following to see what the success rate is with doing the radio-chemo treatment. He tells me afterwards, the chances of eliminating the cancer this way are around 35-50%.

When you start out into a course of treatment like this one, no one really knows what the outcome will be. I went in with a positive force that left no room for anything other than to be successful in clearing out all the cancer cells and allowing for deep transformation of the cells.

This ended up being one of the hardest treatments I had to endure. What got me through the uncomfortable, painful times was the thought that, "If I can stick with this and make each treatment and day really work towards eliminating the tumor cells, I will have many, many days ahead in my life that will make this time worth it."

Maybe I am statistic #901 now. I can be added to the roster of positive cases for trusting and offering other alternative treatments for rectal cancer. Of course, it is more complicated than just looking at a course of treatment and thinking if something worked for this person, it will also work for another person.

As I am learning, each case is highly unique because people present the illness differently, they respond to it in their own way, and they choose their lifestyle while being treated. All of these factors are like a kaleidoscope of color that form their own pattern of healing.

As I was reflecting on my treatment journey before starting chemo again, it dawned on me that had it not been for cancer cells migrating to both my lungs and having to focus so intensely here first, my treatment plan would have gone completely differently. It was imperative to address the many cancer growths in both lungs first before even thinking about the primary tumor and dealing with it.

This bought me 7 months of time. Time which, I now realize, was precious for readjusting my life and redefining my relationship to my body. I was able to intensify my healing by diving into alternative body therapies such as: cranio sacral, energy medicine, EFT (Emotional Freedom Technique or otherwise known as Tapping), deep healing meditations focused around cellular healing, contemplative movement, soul journaling, and mindful mandala coloring.

All of these therapies and healing exercises are focused on unlocking the deep unconscious aspects of the Self while learning to listen more closely to my inner voice or intuition. Cultivating this relationship with Self takes time and the guidance of skilled healers.

When the time came to focus on the primary tumor leading up to the operation, I was able to harness a tidal wave of energy that I had been building over these previous months to now direct toward this next step. Through intense healing sessions, I believe I was able to have a direct impact in shifting my cellular metabolism and live the phrase, "Your belief is your biology."

. . .

My oncologist agreed with me that, had I not had the lungs to deal with first, my treatment route would have been standard procedure and I probably would have had the operation. This was a big revelation for me, to see where I had come from and how perspectives can shift vastly when looked at from a different vantage point.

Now I was feeling so grateful for my lungs, and that they took me on this detour, albeit a rather long and bumpy one. It makes me wonder: there really must be a bigger plan in place for us small humans, and we never know exactly what it is until we can get a little hindsight. So with this gratitude for my lungs, I go into my next follow-up meeting to review the recent CT scan on my lungs.

I was hanging onto the amazing changes my body was going through with regard to the primary tumor and feeling so elated that I had been able to come this far along, and I was still alive.

Never were there any promises of a cure. However, I held onto the possibility of healing and I just knew this was possible. I constantly reminded my specialists of this: healing was my focus, wherever that path took me.

Healing allowed for renewal of my whole life, not just physically but emotionally, mentally and for a greater expansion of my spiritual world. I was exploring all of it. I found I could rebound back from any news I received, regardless of whether it revealed more tumor growth, or less. It was about regenerating my thinking every day, right down to a cellular level.

It wasn't just my body that was my center of attention anymore, it was every aspect of my life.

After enjoying the fabulous news of my remission, my doctor turned towards the CT results. He showed me that one 4 mm lesion had showed up in my left lung. Up until now, every CT scan I had done on my lungs after both operations had shown nothing. I was surprised, and a little disappointed to see this, although my doctor said that it is quite common for leftover nodes to show up that were previously too small to find. This logic was somewhat comforting, but it wasn't really what I wanted to hear and certainly not what my body wanted to know.

I am hoping this new presence is from before, and not new cancer cells. It is there, and something I can't ignore. As I am about to receive more chemo infusions, this development will be watched. There are options to deal with it that are non-invasive and painless so I hold this as a small consolation for new appearances.

I also did a routine blood test for tumor markers, Ferritin (iron), and inflammation before starting my first infusion. I am always keen to track my Ferritin levels because that was the breaking signal for me when I just couldn't think anymore. My levels were so low that now I am always aware of keeping them within a healthy range.

The next day, I received the results in the mail, and I was shocked to see that my tumor marker had risen quite a bit when it had not moved at all since my lung operations. Plus my Ferritin level had dropped substantially.

All of this within a few days of my remission status was knocking me off kilter. I thought to myself, "Can't I just enjoy being in remission feeling healthy and carefree for a little while?" Apparently not!

Life has a way of keeping me on my toes. Trying to take both of these new pieces of information in and process it alongside my big win was tough. Again, I came back to my beginner's mind, leaning into learning how to practice holding all of it in my heart of hearts, with acceptance, non-judgement, and love... this is the moment of being tested.

No one says you have to replace one with the other. I was holding onto the progress I had made and letting go into receiving challenging information. Being with all of it.

The action is to dissolve boundaries of good/bad, negative/positive, healthy/unhealthy, and open up to a wide acceptance of non-judgment and center my body and mind in:

THIS IS LIFE RIGHT NOW, IN THIS MOMENT: JUST BE. Breathe, Breathe, and Breathe Some More.

I made a conscious effort to take a moment to dance with the joy I feel in my body, to love my body as it is and to embrace all that continues to be brought forward into my awareness.

Receiving news that isn't what I wanted to hear and that I immediately place a negative judgment on, is challenging to be with. I don't want to squash all of my excitement and relief in having transformed the pelvic area of my body, yet I need to remain open to the rest of what's going on inside me and kindly and lovingly attend to this as well.

I had a big discussion with my oncologist at our next meeting to talk about both of these new results. I always appreciate and value his perspective because he lives and breathes this slippery balance of life with his patients everyday.

He sees it all: fear, joy, continued life, and the mortality we all face. Death.

He reminds me that I, nor anyone, is ever secure in our health. We think we are, but we're not. Everything can change in an instant. What matters is how we meet this moment and what we do when we receive news that appears unfavorable.

In an instant flash, the shadow of death is hanging out in the corner again. Just when I thought I had gotten rid of you, there you appear as a gentle reminder that you are always walking by my side, helping me make choices, new choices based on new values and priorities that support me to choose life, health, love, and inner freedom.

"You have had a 'Life Intensifier' experience," my oncologist tells me, "and from this, you will never be the same person again."

When he said this, I felt like the Jedi's sword of light ripped through all the old, clingy thinking patterns I was still hanging onto blasting out room for new perspectives and ways of being.

I felt how absolutely right he was! I don't want to be the same person I was.

I WANT TO BE A NEW, INTENSIFIED HUMAN BEING WHO LIVES LIFE EVERYDAY FROM AN OPEN, RELAXED, AND AWARE PLACE. CHOOSING FROM A PLACE OF GREATER LOVE, NOT FROM A PLACE BASED IN FEAR OF DEATH OR THE UNKNOWN.

SOUL ACTIVATION EXERCISE 2: STRONG REASONS FOR LIVING

Let's get you started living a vibrant, intensified life. **What would this look like for you?**

Soul Activation Exercise 2[1] offers you a journaling process that can reveal some exciting surprises. Grab your journal book or something to write in, and let's get going!

What helped me commit to my soul evolving was knowing why I was still here on the planet: What were the strong reasons for me staying alive that kept me going?

This is such an important part of who you are, and being fully aware of it is one of the keys to connecting to your determination and courage when the going gets really tough.

This exercise is designed to help you discover your strong reasons for living. Let them seep into your whole being and then get ready to make your earth connection.

It's important that you don't read ahead to the other parts: do one part at a time.

Part 1) Imagine what you would do with your life if you were guaranteed:

- perfect health to age 100
- unlimited money and resources
- crazy success in whatever you decided to do

Allow yourself to dream BIG!

Think about the areas of your life you'd want to have amazing experiences in. Take into consideration for example:

- Career or volunteering
- Family: how often would you see them? Would you have a family?
- Relationships: who's important to you that you want to have in your life?
- Travel
- Where would you live, what house or houses would you live in?
- Hobbies you would do

Create a picture that includes all the areas of your life that are important to you.

Put on some of your favorite music and take as long as you need for this part. Maybe you have some colored pencils to use as well.

Part 2) Now I ask you this, "What if you were diagnosed with an inoperable blood clot that was absolutely going to explode inside you in a year and a half?" You would have no symptoms up until the point it happened. You'd be perfectly healthy up until that moment and could do anything you wanted to do. You have all the same resources at your disposal that you have today.

What do you do? Do you work? Do you volunteer? Do you travel? What do you do in terms of your family and friends? What would be your final essence of yourself you want to share with the world?

Now without thinking, begin to write down how you would spend the next year and a half.

Again, take your time with this part and only move on when you feel ready.

Part 3) Now begin to go back through part 1 & 2 and look for similarities. If there's the same things or common themes in both parts then this is something to focus on.

If travel or spending time with family is on both, then pay attention to this. You are telling yourself these areas are really important and meaningful to have in your life.

Maybe you're in a wildly successful situation or you're saving the world, this can show you that you want to make a difference for others. It could be in a smaller or larger way. The point is, you have something to share and in sharing your passion, skills, essence, you are making a difference for others.

Reflect on the above, and begin to write and/or draw out the areas that overlap for you. Highlight what you can imagine or already know that brings joy and happiness into your life. You might want to keep what you've written or drawn somewhere that you can read it everyday. Keep your strong reasons for living alive in your heart and at the forefront of your mind.

You are now ready to nurture your earth connection with all of the lifestyle choices in part 2.

Go deeper: Continue your healing journey in my online course, Choose Life!

PART II
CONNECTION

MAKING YOUR EARTH CONNECTION

LIFESTYLE CHOICES MATTER

I quickly realized that within my daily control were the choices I made around how I wanted to live my life.

What kind of lifestyle choices was I making?

Was I aware of what I was choosing, or was I on autopilot, doing what I'd always done before?

Lifestyle is something that is within my control, and when so much felt out of my control, this realization gave me a sense of agency, of being able to be in charge of how I want my day to go.

Lifestyle is now widely recognized as a gamechanger for either supporting a healthy body or one that is compromised by dis-ease. Within the integrative medicine model lifestyle is seen as a 3rd pillar of healing. The other two are conventional allopathic and complementary medicine.

Today, lifestyle choices are so important that it's being called "Lifestyle Medicine."

Even though my lifestyle could be seen as healthy-looking from the outside, I started examining the more subtle aspects of my lifestyle and where I wanted to start making changes.

I had started doing Qigong again and within this movement form, I began to search for a way to connect to the energy of earth and heaven, not just from within, but also when I was outside in nature and ready to soak up the healing energy that is naturally flowing.

Why did this earth connection become so important to me when I was dealing with an illness, one that was demanding many treatments and taxing my body in ways that I had never known before?

Making an earth connection is crucial, as it helps to bring a sense of calmness inside the body and in turn, has the opportunity to still the mind. In times of high stress and uncertainty, the mind tends to go crazy with thoughts that can quickly take you off on a wild goose chase. Finding a way that can calm your body, center you and ground you into this sense of the earth helps to connect you to something greater than yourself.

Mother Earth is a symbol that is calming and nurturing that can handle anything at all. So when you're feeling overwhelmed, or you can't take it anymore and you can't share it with loved ones and those close to you because it just feels like too much, you can always turn to Mother Earth: an image of her that is all encompassing, able to take in any kind of energy and transform it.

Visualize to relax

This is what I would do: I would just let all my angst, worry, and fears go into the earth.

I used a lot of visualizations. I'm a visual person so this was natural for me to do. If it's something that you haven't done before it can feel strange at first but take time to let your imagination focus on an image, and even if you don't see it maybe you feel it or see colors or something else comes to you. Try something different and trust that a simple exercise can bring you to an inner place of peace and calm throughout your body at a time when turbulence is high.

Making a daily earth connection is so critical for healing. Being an active participant in the elements I've outlined below is where deep, daily healing has an opportunity to transform your body, mind, and spirit.

With time and repetition, your body will break down and eliminate what it doesn't need and slowly rebuild back all the strength and wellness that is inherent in the body knowing how to heal itself.

This new level of integration can come by being engaged in all the elements that make up your earth connection.

- Exercise & movement
- Time in nature
- Food & supplements
- Sleep & rest
- Social connections
- Holistic healing support

Exploring all of these elements simultaneously provides a lot of choice in terms of what you want to focus on. Some areas may be a natural fit whereas others will take some extra support. Each area is independent, yet together they are more powerful and provide you with the opportunity to positively influence your quality of life on a daily basis.

Regardless of where you are in your healing journey, you can implement each element into your life in a way that feels right for you. Taking charge of your quality of life is empowering, builds confidence and resilience, and improves your overall sense of wellbeing.

I have come to appreciate and really enjoy making my earth connection part of my daily practice. It's a conscious part of my life now. Enriching my earth connection has helped cultivate a deeper level of integration between all these aspects of my life in a grounded and physical way.

Let's look at what each of these aspects has to offer.

EXERCISE & MOVEMENT

Why is movement so important?

When your body is working hard to heal from an illness while recovering from the side effects of various treatments, movement is important, as it keeps the energy flowing in the body.

Movement may feel like the last thing you want to do when you're sick and not feeling well. Add in various side effects that make you feel nauseous and tired. I know some days all I could do was lay in bed or rest on the sofa. While just laying still is necessary at times, it's not always the best thing to do all of the time.

When the body's tired, the mind can be tired. Sometimes the mind has willpower and says, "Come on, get up, let's go. You need to move." Or what if you're a person that never really liked to exercise, or move too much. You were happy and content sitting or walking a little bit. The reason that movement becomes more important and necessary when you're in a healing phase and you're recovering is to just keep the blood flowing and the muscles limber. The less you use your muscles the weaker you feel and the less you want to do. This becomes a negative feedback loop and one you want to watch you don't get caught up in.

Reborn back into movement

 Qigong is a helpful practice that eventually leads to a deeper experience. In time, the mind becomes one with the stillness of an open heart where it simply watches the qi flowing effortlessly through the body.

— MASTER LI JUNFENG

In treatment, I discovered a whole level of muscle recovery that wasn't discussed when we talked about the logistics of the operation.

Being at the center of treatment and care, I could see how specialized each professional is in his or her job. I admired the depth of knowledge and skill that each one of my doctors and nurses has in their area of specialty. What I learned is that it's up to me to put together a team where my mental, emotional, and spiritual needs are being supported.

The only thing I can relate my lung recoveries to is childbirth. I found out all kinds of information about the actual birthing process and the best ways to manage it. However, I didn't think to ask, and no one told me, what the "afterbirth" time could be like. I was prepared for the actual experience and ready for anything, yet realized I wasn't at all ready for what was to follow.

Nobody told me about cutting nerves and feeling numb across my ribcage, or how tight the muscles can get after they've been forced to stretch beyond their normal range. After the relief of knowing I made it through the 2nd lung operation, I settled into the weeks ahead, hoping to restore my body back to the movement range I was used to.

No recovery is the same. I've had double operations of lungs and hips only to find out that both sides of my body respond differently to the same operation. While I thought I was getting more experienced at recovery, I discovered I wasn't any more prepared for what was to come except that I knew enormous patience was a requirement and that I needed to practice acceptance and self-love towards my body through the unknown path that unfolded.

Yoga gave me a movement foundation that I could look forward to returning back to. However, I noticed that I was careful with every move I made, not to overdo it. I didn't want to cause myself any more pain. I focused on developing my lung capacity with breathing exercises I was given by the physiotherapist and then later with my Qigong exercises.

As the weeks passed and my ribcage started to feel a bit better, I decided to risk a little more movement. I was surprised at how cautious I was to raise my arm up above my head and over to the side, giving my side waist a longer stretch, a movement I had done hundreds of times with ease and always loved the feeling of a good deep side stretch. Now I noticed a hovering of protection and I wasn't as sure of myself to just let my body freely move.

I was cautious and, I realized, a little scared of allowing my body to go ahead and do a stretch that it once knew so well.

I wanted to exercise and start moving again as soon as I could, but I found this wasn't so easy. Not only did I have extremely limited mobility compared to what I was used to, but I was also afraid I'd do something that would hinder my recovery.

Nobody ever talked to me about reclaiming my body after surgery. This is something I'm just discovering now. No matter how careful, skillful, and well-meaning the operating team is, there is trauma to the body and it needs time to mend with care, love, and healing energy. I wanted a physiotherapist to guide me back into an exercise program along with massage and support for helping me gain confidence back to increase my overall movement range.

My oncologist supported this idea as exercise is something that I'm encouraged to be doing. In the early recovery days, I received craniosacral treatments that I found very calming and helped my deeper muscles to begin releasing their tight grip. Slowly, I could begin to feel energy moving through my body.

Cranio-sacral work and massage are helping me to feel that my body can safely move again and have a full range of movement.

Exercise releases endorphins and hormones into your bloodstream that make you feel good and give you energy.

Cardio exercise is a way to increase the oxygen flowing through your cells and cancer is not a friend to oxygen, so while you are gaining strength throughout your muscles and mobility, your cells are being flushed with increased oxygen eliminating cancer cells.

I began introducing more body movement by laying on my yoga mat at home and just allowing my body to freely move and to gently explore how far I could stretch. Doing this helped me to build confidence back into my body's ability to heal.

I accepted that it's natural to feel afraid to move fully and freely after an operation, but it's not fun to be stuck in fear of movement.

Regaining trust and confidence in your body to move, to be healed, and to feel good is so important for the journey back to vibrant health. Listening to your body is vitally important to know what you need for help along the way and when you're ready to try the next stretch.

Four weeks after my second lung operation I reached up towards the sky into Tree Pose on January 1st and at seven weeks I was able to gently press myself up into Downward Dog. In between, I took advantage of some snow that fell in our backwoods and went for a short cross-country ski while my kids walked beside me. The body surprises, don't be held back by fear in the mind. The mind will get on board when it realizes the body is capable and then you can start having more fun!

As movement recovery becomes more stable in your body, committing to a daily practice using a variety of movement activities and exercises becomes a valuable discipline to support your overall health, strength, and a positive mood.

Creating a daily and weekly calendar helps you begin to exercise especially on those days when you're not feeling so energized. Once you begin, the rest follows naturally and you finish feeling better for having moved your body.

What are the types of movement that you like to do or dream of doing?

You get to choose. Doesn't matter what it is, as long as it's something.

I'd like to suggest a couple of different forms of movement. One kind of movement is more reflective, more contemplative, maybe you could even call it a little more meditative such as Qigong, tai chi, yoga, or a contemplative dance or authentic dance style where you get to follow your body's inner rhythm.

Mindful walking helps synchronize your mind and body. Your mind can feel clear and empty of thoughts, worries, and concerns as you focus your thoughts on each step. Maybe even in this clear space, a decision comes to you or something you've been thinking about wondering how you were going to get through.

I came across a form of Qigong called Sheng Zhen developed by Master Li Junfeng. I've been practicing a series of contemplations that include movement and sitting meditations. Practicing Qigong outside is my favorite classroom to be in. The endless space of the universe surrounds me while I use my imagination to connect to all the natural elements.

I feel my feet on the ground. I look towards the sky and reach my arms out with open hands to take in all the energy around me. As thoughts come up in my mind, I let them go like passing clouds. My body feels filled up with the natural beauty around me and with each breath I take, my muscles relax, my nervous system slows down, and my heart becomes quiet and full of love. In this moment I feel my body, mind, and spirit become one with nature and the universe at large. There are no limits to this feeling of expansiveness.

The body has been energized and relaxed at the same time. The positive, feel good hormones are being released and this is giving your immune system a boost. You are also sending life affirming messages to your cells.

When the body softens and opens up, the mind becomes quiet and spacious. It is easier to notice how you're feeling and merge with the natural surroundings around you. A blade of grass, flowers in bloom, birds singing in the trees. Depending on the season and where you live, your environment will be unique for the time of year and geography. Observe all that is around you.

As you connect to the natural environment, an energetic link is felt between you, the earth, and the space beyond your body into the atmosphere, up toward the heavens. This becomes the beauty that happens practicing Qigong, especially outside. Feeling a oneness between the natural forces that we live with all the time and letting go into that Universal Life Force trusting and surrendering into it.

Being open to what happens. Feeling the synchronization of your breath with the movement, being outside and feeling the air and the temperature opening up your skin pores, allowing all your senses to receive energy as you synchronize your breath with your movement. Taking in all the energy around you is as easy as opening the windows of your home to let the fresh breeze blow through.

Adjusting your awareness in this way with accompanying movements slowly builds up energy and the immune system. You learn to trust that your body can still move and do so many things. There's still so much happening in your body that is healthy and functioning well. Remember, there is more right with you than there is wrong!

I took time as often as possible, ideally a little bit every day, with contemplative practices like Qigong and gentle yoga. Engaging in more physical forms of exercise was something I aimed to do three or four times a week when my body allowed for it.

It is wonderful when you surprise yourself by moving in a way you thought your body wasn't up to. Maybe it's going for a walk or a bike ride, or going out to play in the snow.

When you're fully engaged in some movement activity and enjoying yourself, then you can be sure that positive hormones are being released throughout your body. Increased joy and happiness abounds and life feels wonderful no matter what your situation is. This is something to celebrate.

GETTING INTO NATURE

Winter had arrived, and I was going away for the first time since I was diagnosed with cancer and started all my chemo treatments and surgeries. February was traditionally a ski week break from school and we'd go away with a group of friends and their ski crazy offspring to enjoy the mountains. This year we re-visited Chamonix.

The sky is a brilliant blue, the big mountains of the Chamonix-Mont-Blanc take their place in the skyline exuding a powerful stillness that my vision never tires of.

The excitement of being able to ski again overrode any concern about snow conditions. The weather forecast was for full sun and no snow. Sun in these mountains is as good as gold as far as I'm concerned.

Being able to wake up in the morning and have Mont Blanc quietly sitting above me and the skyline of jagged peaks stretched out before my eyes was something I couldn't wait to take in.

There really is something about being healed in beautiful environments, like taking in the view of a lake and mountains from a hospital bed. We can't ignore the healing power of how our body and mind respond to natural beauty when we are enveloped in it.

I telemark ski, which is typically more demanding on the whole body than downhill alpine skiing. My first tele-ski day came exactly ten weeks after my second lung surgery. I had been preparing mentally for this day and this week for a long time and was so excited to get out in the mountains. I wanted to get back into my ski gear and enjoy that feeling of floating down the mountain with each turn.

We started at Le Tour, an area we've skied before and enjoyed for its wide open area with lots of area to ski off-piste. The runs are relatively short which is good for my first day on the slopes. I was a little nervous about skiing because I had no idea how my body would feel. I am still recovering in my ribcage and diaphragm area and I really haven't had much time to get my legs in tele shape. I discovered there's nothing like doing to get the feeling back!

The body is amazing at remembering what it's good at. Back on the skis, I felt strong, like I hadn't missed a turn! I kept telling my body how incredible it was, and what a good job it was doing!

Your body works hard for you and needs a lot of reassurance and pats on the back. Once you've had your body go through something major like being cut open in surgery, it's incredible how the body's laser focus finds its way back to its original healthy blueprint.

To me, I experience it as a miracle knowing how much I was stripped down to being completely dependent on the care of others to eventually bouncing back to my inner strength again.

We returned from our ski week and I was scheduled to see my oncologist for my next round of chemo. He said it was clear that the mountains were good for me and I even put on some weight, all muscle of course!

My next operation was April 7th, and I was reminded by my doctor to make sure to take time to be in the mountains before heading into the next surgery. What makes the Spirit strong is a big plus for pre-surgery prep.

How do you enjoy nature? What makes your body and heart sing?

Depending on the season and the environment you live in, nature provides different opportunities. Maybe you live by the ocean and morning walks to see the sunrise give you energy. I know for me, just looking at pictures of ocean sunrises or sunsets gives me a warm and peaceful feeling.

If getting outside is difficult for you at certain times, then bring nature to you. Increase the plants and flowers in your home. Get pictures of nature that you love, and put on a slideshow of nature pictures on your computer monitor or TV. Be creative and find ways to bring more natural beauty to you.

FOOD & INTUITIVE EATING

 Let food be thy medicine and medicine be thy food.

— HIPPOCRATES

When news arrived that I had cancer, I immediately thought, *"It's time to tighten up my food choices to more effectively support my body with powerful anti-cancer ingredients!"*

This is when I really took to heart the encouragement I kept receiving from the doctor's: *listen to what your body wants to eat.* Losing weight was a concern for me, so I had to balance what I could eat with top quality calories, meaning more coconut in all forms, avocados, and nut butters.

My food preferences have evolved as I was faced with different aspects of my cancer journey. Food choices are extremely personal and something that a person needs to be 100% in favor of. The biggest change I had to make was opening up my mind and being willing to listen to what my stomach was telling me.

I began to pay close attention to the foods that helped me feel calm and stable inside, and the foods that aggravated my digestion. This became a pressing topic quickly due to the chemotherapy and the side effects.

I read up on different kinds of anti-cancer diets, but I found it difficult to suddenly start changing what I was eating in the midst of going through weekly recoveries from chemo infusions.

Has your eating changed as you've gone through various treatments, or has it remained the same? I found that when I focused on trying to choose the best diet to help my body, I became more confused, as each type of diet had its own pros and cons. My guiding question became: *What feels right for me at this time?* I could always change it later.

Whether my doctor's training was western allopathic or complimentary, they all said the same thing with regards to my diet:

Eat what feels right for you, listen to your body.

As a general rule, I kept my sugar intake low and ate whole foods, fresh and organic as much as I could manage. I was already thrown into so many adjustments with replacing a regular work routine with medical appointments and intensive treatments I knew I couldn't handle changing anything else in my life at the time as it created more stress for me.

The idea of listening to my body for what food to eat wasn't entirely new to me. I routinely used to come home from work and either go for a walk or a run and on that outing always come home with an idea for dinner. While I was out in the fresh air, exercising, I would tune in to what it was I felt like eating that night and always a picture or idea for a meal would come to me by time I got back home.

I had to let go of trying to do everything "right" around food. I was aware of the Ketogenic diet for cancer and had read a lot of very positive articles about how it had helped people heal their cancer and strongly considered following it. But I found myself counting carbs all the time, and realizing that it was a losing battle trying to keep the numbers down. Even having a cappuccino had carbs in the milk and this was a drink I really enjoyed.

Eating the right way became a bigger stressor for me emotionally, preventing me from simply being able to enjoy whatever I was eating or drinking. I had to change my mindset and let go of this pressure I was creating in order to find a calmer state.

I was reminded that, "It's better to be happy and enjoy the food you're eating rather than beating yourself up for overindulging or choosing something that you think is too sweet, too fat, too many carbs, etc, etc."

Cancer expresses itself in very personal ways making each healing journey a unique path of transformation.

What I've come to find out about cancer is that it's a very personal manifestation in one's body and how it expresses itself. There is not one fix for all and while there's value in reading how other people are eating for anti cancer, you then need to ask yourself, "What feels right for me?"

Listen to your intuition and trust that you know the path to follow. I am grateful that I work with health care specialists and natural health doctors who continue to remind me that it's so vitally important to listen to your intuition, trust what your body is telling you. I want to honor my body's needs, so I have been listening and listening and listening.

Food requirements continue to change over the months. I started out with a very strict, plant-based diet, and then because I was going to have two surgeries fairly close together, the doctors didn't want me to lose any more weight. I was trying to stabilize my weight after losing 9kgs. I'm not a big person, and every kilo counts.

After two months of plant-based only, I decided to include spelt flour so I could have a slice of bread every day. I think this was partly driven by the weather changing and moving deeper into Fall. I wanted slightly heavier foods.

Funny enough, a soft boiled egg on toast was something I was craving so I decided to give myself some latitude and have an egg and toast for breakfast in the morning. Turned out I enjoyed it so much that I added avocado on the toast and some mornings spread on goat cheese as well, topped with sprouts.

It's important to find healthy foods that your body responds well to and then to enjoy eating them. Keeping on weight is an important part of the healing journey.

In the end, I observed how my digestive system handled food, how my overall body felt, and my mood. It's important to be honest with yourself, listen to your inner voice, do your research, and then allow your intuition to help guide your choices.

Shopping became more intentional. Though I was never a big consumer of processed or pre-made foods, I deliberately stopped buying anything that was already made in a jar or package, no matter how healthy the ingredients were. Only whole, fresh foods, and grains came into our house. I dove into two vegan cookbooks and started trying out many of the recipes.

I loved how these recipes combined a lot of the foods I already ate, but in different combinations from what I was used to. The use of dates in many recipes surprised me as a form of sweetener. I love dates, but didn't eat them that often. I had cut out all sugar completely in the first few months, but eventually I loosened up and started using dates in some recipes.

I've had fun making different desserts like Sweet Potato Brownies with almond butter and coconut icing, or Broccoli, Avocado & Lime salad. I get inspired by recipes, and as I follow them, I usually adjust them a little. With the Broccoli and Avocado salad, I added pomegranate seeds, arugula, and lightly steamed kale. These additions made for an excellent lunch or really nice dinner salad. Don't be afraid to alter recipes with some of your favorite foods or whatever is calling to you from the fridge.

It was after a PET/CT scan in March that showed continued small spots or possibly lesions in my lungs that I revisited what I was eating. I pulled out my stored information on the ketogenic diet. I had first looked at it when I started chemotherapy, but back then I didn't have the mental resolve to follow such a precise way of eating. Now, I was feeling ready for this new challenge.

Keto for Cancer

Going on a keto diet for Cancer is quite specific in terms of how many carbs, protein, and fat you're allowed to take in.

The caloric intake is dependent on your weight, height, age and amount of exercise you do.

Fats

To increase the 'good' fats, I started slowly introducing different nut oils into my daily eating such as: avocado, almond, chia, and macadamia. Also MCT (Medium-Chain Triglyceride) oil, which is excellent for keto diets and is derived from coconut.

I dropped all grains because of their high carb content, including my favorite Tuscan beans. Needing more concentrated protein sources, I went back to eating organic chicken and having fish or seafood 1-2 times a week, as well as increasing my egg consumption. My bean soup was replaced with a comforting chicken and vegetable soup.

Breads are also tricky, however, the keto community has found a way around this by making bread with almond flour and coconut flour. This is a completely satisfying alternative to grain-based bread, and very filling.

Sugar

Cancer cells cannot thrive without sugar, and so, in a simplistic, cellular way of thinking, I knew I should just stop eating refined sugar.

But while I am not a big sugar fan, I loved my apple a day and baked pear cobbler. On a keto diet, though, fruits are out except for small amounts of berries: blueberries, raspberries, or strawberries. There simply is too much sugar in them, even though it's natural. Eating in a keto style calls for finding some creativity around the sugar issue.

With some research, we discovered that there is a form of sweetener that doesn't raise blood sugar in the same way as other sugars: Erythritol. I found a product called Swerve in Canada, a decent tasting sweetener that works for baking. I have also found a sugar replacement that is a mix of Erythritol (Erythrit in German) and Stevia in Switzerland called Stevia Sweet. With both these sugar replacements, I am able to satisfy my chocolate chip cookie cravings!

My other favorite treat is dark chocolate. Very dark, as in 80% and higher. This requires the taste buds to adjust, but it is very satisfying and its bonus qualities are: high in protein and fiber with a much lower carb/sugar count than dark chocolate that is 70% and below.

It's not so hard to let other foods go when I can find comfort and satisfaction in a few well-chosen items!

From Cow to Sheep & Goat

Sugar also comes in the form of carbohydrates, and in almost all foods there are some carbs. This is why grains and legumes are put on the sidelines in a keto diet.

Sheep's milk has a better ratio of fats & proteins to carbohydrates than cow's or even goat's milk.

And sheep and goat cheeses are easier to digest and less prone to creating inflammation in the body than their cow's milk counterparts.

I found it surprisingly easy to stop eating all cow-based dairy. I even discovered that I preferred sheep dairy to cow, and started using sheep milk for my cappuccinos. Sheep dairy products are surprisingly mild and can be used just like regular milk.

My one cow dairy cheat is: whipping cream. Full fat dairy is actually a bonus when it comes to the keto way, so I have embraced my whipping cream!

I share these quirky eating habits with you because I'm only human and I like to find foods I enjoy within the boundaries of this particular diet. I don't want to feel like I have to cut out the few foods I really enjoy otherwise, there's just no fun left in eating!

Eat With Enjoyment

Intentionally enjoying food creates a more receptive feeling in the body to receive what's being taken in. Deliberately developing mindful eating habits begins to cultivate an appreciation for a time to slow down, relax, and feel grateful for what is in front of you.

There are always many other things a person is doing to work on their treatment and recovery plans, and if eating becomes just another stressful task to undertake, then the healing potential that can take place from the food is sacrificed. Listening to your intuitive voice (and stomach) while respecting the scientific and cellular information is the challenge.

This is a fine balance that I am still eating my way through! It's a process, and one I've had to accept with greater self-compassion for where I'm at. I am still enjoying eggs, and these are great on a keto diet. While trying to figure out how to eat my egg without bread one morning, I put together a soft boiled egg inside half an avocado and added a few sprouts. This turned out to be a delicious and satisfying first meal of the day filled with lots of good fats, protein and very little carbs.

Challenges

Finding a balance between sticking to a way of eating and listening to my body is the biggest challenge for me. I have read numerous cancer healing stories about people eating all kinds of different foods and healing themselves from their cancer. Probably not just on food alone, but it seemed to be a significant factor among their healing protocols.

I wonder, does simply believing in what you're eating constitute a healing factor, or is it the food that supports your cells in strengthening your immune system that can then go and deal with the cancer cells, or is it a combination of both?

I found it extremely challenging to keep my carb intake down to the very low suggested count of 12 per day that is needed to get your body into ketosis, a state of burning fat for fuel instead of sugar. This metabolic action kicks in when you have basically starved your cells of sugar and the healthy cells now start looking to use fat as their energy source.

In order to really know how many carbs, proteins, and fats you get everyday, you must measure and weigh out everything you eat. I find this tedious and a challenge to do. I realized it's not my personality to be so specific with everything I eat. When I tried to do this, it just made me not want to eat anymore so I wouldn't have to deal with figuring out all the math!

Eating in such a specific way took away the creativity and spontaneity for me, and slowly I noticed that I became less interested in putting a meal together. My level of mental stress around eating was also weighing heavily on me. I'm still working to find a way that helps me be more easily aware of how many carbs, fat, and protein I'm actually taking in.

There are different stages of ketosis and for cancer diets, the goal is to be in a "higher state" of ketosis. Cancer cells do not have metabolic flexibility like the healthy cells do, so their ability to survive begins to die out. This is my very simplistic explanation, and I recommend doing your own research if you are interested in this diet for anti-cancer. There is a lot of information available.

I believe strongly in using the best of ALL medicines that are available and I found that, to my surprise, drugs and natural medicine can and do complement one another to achieve an even more powerful healing transformation. This is the transformative power of Integrated Medicine.

Throughout my exploration with food, I kept coming back to trying to understand more deeply how nutrition enhances my intuition and how intuition enhances my nutrition. This question has led me into a whole new way of eating.

Listening to what my body wants to eat every day, rather than what my mind says to eat, has developed into a small obsession.

After doing the keto diet, I was introduced to a very interesting and mind-expanding book written by Anthony William, the Medical Medium, called *Life-Changing Foods: Save Yourself and the Ones You Love with the Hidden Healing Powers of Fruits and Vegetables.*

William writes about The Holy Four food groups: Fruits, Vegetables, Herbs & Spices, and Wild Foods. There are 50 chosen foods each highlighted with a summary about the food in general, the health conditions and symptoms the food can help with and also summaries about the emotional support and spiritual lesson each food offers.

This approach to food was new to me and helped me begin considering a wider range of healing possibilities through food.

When I was recovering in the hospital, Geoff was bringing me fresh food every night for my dinner. The food he made felt and tasted 100% fresher and full of healing properties compared to the hospital food. I remember asking him to bring me avocados mashed up with fresh lime juice squeezed on top, nothing else. This tasted so incredibly nourishing and good to me, I couldn't eat enough of it. I love avocados, but this was like a whole new experience of eating one for me.

Was it because my body was so weak and in need of comfort, nutrition, and support in every way it could get it that I was perhaps more mindful of what I was eating now?

Avocados are one of the chosen 50 foods in Anthony Williams book. He writes about the spiritual lesson of the avocado and says, "Avocados are all about nurturing, it is the mother fruit, the closest food on the planet to breast milk." He writes about avocados as the ultimate comfort food and to "bring avocados in your life as a teacher of unconditional love, both toward yourself and others and watch your capacity for compassion grow and flourish."[1]

When I read this after I had my own experience eating avocados, I knew what he was talking about on a level that I could not rationally explain. When your body is completely at the mercy of needing greater help than you can give it alone, any defensive walls give way to a place of vulnerability, acceptance, and possibility. This is when you can open up to the healing power of foods.

Finally, my food was my medicine, and my medicine was my food. I felt Hippocrates' words in my body, soul, and spirit on those days of recovering in the hospital and now I can't let go of the potential for how much food can heal the body. I am hungry for more recipes and knowledge of how foods do heal our bodies and increase our ability to connect to our intuition.

I look forward to creating meals every day whether it's a combination of fruit and veggies for juices, salads, soups, or desserts. Approaching cooking with mindful awareness is healing for the body and comforting for the soul.

Having time to prepare meals and enjoy them slowly and mindfully has slowed me down to cook with more intention, to notice how my body feels after eating different foods, and to ask myself, did that meal enhance my energy and support clarity in my mind or did it make me feel tired and foggy in my head?

You always have a choice of what you put into your body.

Whatever you are choosing to ingest, do it wholeheartedly and with a mindful focus.

SUPPLEMENTS FOR ANTI-CANCER SUPPORT

Having extra vitamin and supplement support is something I have always done, so it was a natural step for me to explore how else I could incorporate this aspect of healing into my overall treatment program.

In the early days after my diagnosis, we discovered an integrative oncologist who specialized in protocols using supplements to enhance any kind of treatment program. A focus of Dr. LaValley's recommendation was to use vitamins, herbs, and repurposed drugs to enhance and synergize the healing potential with chemotherapy drugs and complementary treatments such as with the hyperthermia bed.

This became a whole other path that I followed diligently and was integrated into my eating routine. It was very meticulous how I had to ingest so many pills and looking back I see that a lot of my mental energy around eating and food went into managing this daily protocol I did.

One of the things I learnt from Dr. LaValley doing this program was about safety and tolerance. I had to listen to my body carefully for feedback all the time. I could be taking 60 pills over the course of a 24 hour period and needed to be keeping track of when I took them and how many. I also wrote down everything I ate, how I felt physically and emotionally and if I had any discomfort or symptoms showing up.

Dr. LaValley was an incredible teacher and made something that at first looked impossible to do absolutely possible with the tracking system he'd created.

The theme of putting my safety first and monitoring for tolerance levels really started seeping into me. The practice of keeping such a close track of taking all of the health supplements was really good for me because it made me write down and track how I felt, what I noticed and observed. He stressed that the first time I start to feel a change that is different from my baseline is when I stop taking the supplements and wait until I return to 'normal' again. In other words, stop taking the supplements before my body reacts too strongly to them.

The idea was not to wait until symptoms became so uncomfortable or the problem became too big. It was vitally important to stop taking them before I got to this point. I began to transfer this approach to my life. Why wait until something is so uncomfortable or a bigger issue? Stop and make changes right away. Adjust the course of action. This was another truth for how to live life!

How often do I go on and push forth when I'm tired, aching, or feeling sick? It's a habit that just becomes ingrained so that even when I do notice something is off, I may do a little extra meditation or yoga, but I don't stop what I'm doing... I keep going.

This is what got me to where I am now. Going along for days, weeks, months not feeling quite right, knowing that something was off with my body, but just accepting it as working and being tired.

How do I distinguish between what kind of tired I am feeling? Is it from work, taking care of kids, or simply getting older? It's hard to know exactly and my habit has been to keep going on and on dragging myself through the day. This is not a healthy strategy and I've discovered this the hard way. The very hard way!

You take care of yourself by listening to your body and making a choice with the information you receive. Not doing anything is a choice, however not always a helpful one and can lead to damaging and bigger problems.

Diving into this protocol regime is another step towards taking care of myself in a new way, more diligently and honestly. Saying to myself, I will watch out for you and put your safety first and not allow you to tolerate any discomforts.

Carolyn Myss talks a lot about your honor code and are you respecting it. Knowing your values and beliefs about what's deeply important and non-negotiable for your own wellbeing is a vital component of the honor code.

My "honor code" embodies being kind and loving to my Self in all ways every day. This is a turning point and a critical step in long term healing and continuous health.

SOCIAL CONNECTIONS

A dis-eased body is a disruption in the flow of energy and to me, says time for a thorough cleansing. My mind wants to clean the house, make the temple shine again.

How to do this? It is not easily done alone. Helpers are needed, people who are part of your extended tribe, who you may have at one point, shared a meal or a laugh with.

What I found, and you may find this too, is that when you're first diagnosed with an illness that your social connections with others can dramatically shift, especially if you have a really difficult diagnosis of cancer, or any other illness where you're going to need all kinds of support.

I was working in a busy, high school of 500 Kids and 50 staff when I was diagnosed. I knew everybody. I had a lot of friends, acquaintances and colleagues. I had no idea what kind of support I was going to need and it was hard to imagine needing so much help because I was used to doing everything on my own.

What I noticed right away were the friends and colleagues who stepped in and said they wanted to help me. All the offerings of help took me by surprise. I thought, well, why not? If people are coming from their heart and they have something to offer that can help make this new journey a little softer and easier then I had to learn to open up to it and receive their offerings.

One of the things a colleague did for me right away was to create a WhatsApp circle of immediate friends, where we could coordinate the logistics. I realized there was a whole new kind of logistical list that needed to happen I had no idea about. Some of the questions needing answers were:

- Who was going to drive me to my chemo appointments?
- Who would stay with me or who was going to pick me up?
- Who wanted to make some food for me?
- Who wanted to take me to a doctor's appointment?
- Who wanted to just come over for a visit?

My husband Geoff was working as a teacher at the school, and it was impossible for one person to do all these things I needed. Many hands made the logistics much easier and I also received the benefits of deepening friendships and unique shared experiences.

I had such little energy for anything that I was not in a position to say, "No thanks, I don't need your help," because I did. I really did. My circle of support quickly grew and I had plenty of help.

Having this kind of support made me wonder why we don't naturally help each other out more often. It's so easy to get caught up in our own world and feel overwhelmed with everything that needs to be done, we don't think about either asking for some help or checking in with others if they could use a hand.

The WhatsApp group made it easy for people to have access to what was needed and how they could help. It took the pressure off me and allowed people to participate or not.

I realized I also wanted the virtual support of so many close friends who were scattered around the world. I originally wanted to start a blog as a way to invite these friends to stay connected with me. My idea of starting a blog was taking much longer and proving more difficult for me to do on my own. In fact, the technical aspect of it was stressing me out more than dealing with my cancer treatments!

When I was preparing for my first lung operation I wanted to get in touch with many close friends around the world and let them know what was happening with me and to ask for their prayers and positive healing thoughts towards me. This was going to be the first operation I'd ever had and I really didn't know what I was in for. I intuitively felt that I needed all the support I could get from near and far.

I had lived overseas for 12 years and made friends all over the world. We largely were connected through Facebook. I had just heard of it when we were leaving Kuwait to move to Shanghai, China and although I was reluctant about signing up for it, I saw it as an easy way to stay in touch with my newfound friends. The hook for me was, it will help me stay connected and be able to communicate easily.

It became clear to me that my blog post was not going to be up in time so, I resorted to creating a group on messenger. Honestly, I thought it would be an inconvenience to everyone in the group because who wants to be bothered by lots of beeps on their phone? I had to just get over what they'd think and invite them to the group.

Without realizing it, I was connecting people living all over the world: China, New Zealand, Canada, Africa, United Emirates, United States, Luxembourg, Singapore, Indonesia, Germany, Hong Kong, Abu Dhabi, France, Portugal, Switzerland, and India.

There became so many options for being connected to others whether it was through social media or in person, I just felt the urge to make the avenues possible and then people can choose how they want to interact and stay informed.

Social connections can change as you go through the journey of getting better from an illness. This can apply to online or live communication. Some people may find it really hard to deal with a complex cancer journey emotionally, they're not sure how they can help and that's okay.

I had no extra energy to analyze or over-think what other people needed. I trusted that they were taking care of their needs emotionally. If they needed to have their own space and not be with me, that was fine. I had plenty of support around me, and new support was coming in all the time. I trusted life was going to support me and just went with the flow of how each day was unfolding. I received energy from the people who had it to give and that was a beautiful exchange of sharing, support, and love. It was an energy exchange where we both felt the value of being together.

I didn't need to know what everybody was getting for themselves from connecting with me or what I was getting from them. As long as it felt right in my heart that was all that mattered. People naturally find their comfort zones in terms of dealing with something very intense and especially for family members.

I wanted to include more close friends into my journey yet I wasn't feeling ready to send out a general post on my Facebook status at this time.

I felt my boundaries were being pushed in terms of opening up my life to the internet.

Communicating in this digital world was bringing up questions around how much I was comfortable sharing. I really had to wrestle with my thoughts around weighing the benefits of communicating on a wider scale as opposed to keeping my circle small. Eventually, I arrived at a place of acceptance and took the chance to post.

I know I fall into a different category with digital communication. I'm in my 50's, and didn't grow up in the digital age. I was brought up to write letters by hand, put them in the mail with a stamp, and send them off. The first time my children had to send a letter for something was when they were in university and they had to ask me where to get stamps from.

So different, what we grow up with and become accustomed to in just a couple of decades!

Another benefit I realized was that I could even have a friend send out a message on this group if I didn't have the energy to. All of these small realizations added up to creating a hub of communicating that felt so real and visceral. I felt the benefits quickly exceeding any fears I had around over-sharing through the internet.

The first initial message came out on the 3rd of November 2016. Here is what I wrote:

> *Hi Everyone! I know this is not terribly personal, sending updates this way, but my blog creation is taking longer than I'd like to get up and running due to my digital abilities. :) So for now, I'll just be able to send out one update to you all for this next week, and so you can help me by focusing some positive healing energy my way on Monday November 7th when I go in for surgery in the morning on my left lung to remove the lung meds that spread there. You can reply back individually to me if you like, but I just wanted you to have this info as I know you are probably wondering what's up? I will open up to receiving your positive energy and love.*
>
> *I just found out today that my CT scan did show the cancer growths shrinking after 4 weeks of chemo and 7 weeks of other complementary therapies. So this is good news! Treatments and everything I have been doing is helping my body to deal with the growths and begin to dissolve and disintegrate the cancer cells. This Monday, I will go in for the 1st planned surgery and be in the hospital for the whole week recovering. It's not a huge procedure but it being a lung, they need to make sure I can breathe properly. Geoff will have time off work to be around the hospital. It's on the other side of the lake and is supposed to be a lovely place.*

Pictures will tell. Will be in touch. Big hugs and love from the Swiss Alps!

This was my first distance digital healing circle. I didn't know at the time what a powerful circle it was going to become.

People didn't write to me individually, they just all jumped onto the same thread and shared their love and support. Over time, I felt like we all became an extended global family. There are literally hundreds of messages on this one group and I can say for myself, that reading them during critical times like pre and post surgeries, meant more to me than reading any other book.

I want to share some of the messages that came to me so you can feel the power of love and support that comes through the energy of the words.

Sending you love and healing energy from Santa Cruz.

Healing, loving energy vibrating into your body and soul has been sent from Shanghai to you.

Sending healing vibes from Myanmar.

You've given me so much strength by sharing your journey, for fearlessly being who you are no matter what and shining your bright light through the most unimaginable tough times you've gone through.

Inspired by your strength and compassion, sending love and hugs.

I have learned so much about determination, self-empowerment, and love from your journey.

Fantastic progress! Well done on all the hard work you're doing in recovery.

Through this beautiful group, I experienced the true power of what the digital world can offer in ways where you never feel alone in your suffering, yet even better, you are buoyed up with energy, strength, and hope to keep going.

I just scrolled through all of them as I'm writing and it is amazing for me to re-read so many heartfelt, uplifting, positive, love, and light-filled messages. Who wouldn't feel good receiving messages like this!

For this reason alone, I have developed a new relationship with my iPhone. Not being able to work and being a person who values connection with others, I have found meaningful ways to connect through phone apps.

Don't be afraid to reach out through these apps and the myriad of ways to connect digitally regardless of your age. You will be surprised at how much energy you can receive!

For local friends to whom I wanted to send out one message, I created a separate WhatsApp group. Again, this made it easy to let friends know how I was doing and to receive their support virtually. I found this is also a great way to receive support from friends when I was too tired to actually have visitors. It helped keep me connected in a wonderful circle of love.

These virtual connections really kept me going until I had enough energy to visit with people. I didn't realize how much energy it took to be with another person talking and just being together.

My energy levels were stripped down to zero and I had to be very mindful using what I had for healing and not overextending my capacity for being with others. This was a new balance I had to learn as I'd never considered it before.

New apps for communicating hit the market all the time. Find the one that is easiest for you and just go for it. Most of them incorporate a video function so it's possible to see who you're talking to. This is a feature I've always valued, especially for family members who are living far away.

I still sent out some emails to a few family friends who are not on these digital platforms and I even received some cards in the mail. There's nothing sweeter than looking in my mailbox to see my friends' handwriting on an envelope instead of the usual typed-out addresses that for me this year represent medical bills and statements!

Over the summer while I had time to recover from treatments, I decided to sign up for an Instagram account. A little slow to jump into this app, but I knew some of my friends and kids checked this more than Facebook, so I thought, *"Why not?"* Another way to connect with the world.

Soon after I was on Instagram, my daughter sent me a link to someone who she thought I would connect with: a total stranger. I was open minded about it and while I normally wouldn't follow up on something like this, I did. It was another woman going through cancer treatments and sharing her story in similar creative ways to how I have processed my journey. I was instantly attracted and curious about her journey.

I have found something very powerful connecting to people along similarly difficult and uncertain paths through our virtual world. Time, space, and physical presence are not relevant for this connection. We connect on another plane of existence that for me is just as meaningful and heartfelt as knowing someone in person.

What a revelation, to experience this as a new truth in our world and how it opens up the possibilities for touching others' hearts!

Social connections remained an important factor that helped contribute to my overall healing. Each one is valuable as it becomes part of the integrated whole that makes up my healing journey and each individual's personal journey.

Emotional support from others was critical whether it was in person, over the phone or through a text. Being able to connect through conversations, let go and cry, share a warm hug and then be able to carry on to enjoy life was critical. Several seasons lapsed and this allowed for many opportunities to cultivate new ways of being with one another.

Although I honestly didn't have much energy available to be supporting others and their process, I did acknowledge that being on the outside of an illness is so hard for the people who love you and don't want to lose you in their life.

This is an entirely new situation for everyone involved, it's something they can't fix or find a quick solution for. It's a real predicament that forces everyone to find their own place of patience, trust, and holding onto hope as each day brings new information.

No one escapes dealing with the fear of what if, what if she dies and this, in turn, makes one's own mortality all the more real. It's an uncomfortable and scary place to be sitting alone with your fear of losing someone you love, knowing that one day you will transition on as well, and wondering about everything that will happen in between. This is one of the reasons I was open to having conversations with anyone who wanted to talk about their fears, worries, or concerns and give space to the unsettled and uncertain emotions.

I had close women friends I would call together for healing meditations especially around times when surgeries would come up and during recoveries. We would set intentions for the best possible outcomes for my body and for a strong spirit. These were intimate and sacred circles when we gathered to build up a vortex of energy for healing and the upcoming procedure. These happened in person as well as virtually.

Being held in a prayer circle or a healing circle, however you want to name it, was very uplifting and centering. The energy was flowing and I really felt it benefiting all those sending the energy to me and receiving it. I was very grateful for these gatherings.

Birthing and Breathing has been the healing theme that emerged for me this year, due largely in part to where I had to focus my energy and the targeted treatment areas. There has been a strong feminine force evolving all year around this and so it came to me that a celebration of Sisterhood was needed. Not to negate all the amazing support I have received from the men in my life. I took in the male energy of clarity, discernment, focus, practicality & strength, and a tenderness that have all opened the way for me to weave more deeply, these qualities into my feminine self.

More celebrations will come to include everyone however, this time marks a completion; an embracing of feminine qualities such as nurturance, commitment to life, grace, loving compassion, understanding, and taking wise action.

To mark this passage and the turning of a new year for me in September, we joined together for an evening of food, bellydancing, and laughter.

I am now the same age my Dad passed away and I feel a quiet and knowing connection with him. I feel as if I have made it past a threshold and will be living many more years.

I have arrived at the top of one of the many mountains I've climbed this year. Resting and taking in the panoramic view, I quiet my mind to allow the vast, open space before me to be reflected back into my being. To find stillness in the silence, to listen for how I want to move forward with my global family. To mark the closure of a journey well traveled, and to find my next steps as I continue to align my expression in the world through soul, body, and mind.

SLEEP AND REST

> Put your thoughts to sleep, do not let them cast a shadow over the moon of your heart. Let go of thinking.
>
> — RUMI

I spent a lot of time sleeping, knowing that it gave my body time to regenerate and have the freedom to be focused on healing without my mind getting in the way. Sleep has always been a balm for me. A place to go and forget about earthly constraints and give way into another world where everything feels perfect. Sleep was another way of giving my body time to do what it needed to do and I trusted the amount of time I needed even when it felt like I was sleeping a lot.

What was more challenging for me was learning how to rest. As soon as I felt a surge of energy I wanted to get up and go. Maybe I felt fit enough for a bike ride, a walk, or a visit with a friend.

What I realized over time was that I needed to learn to accept a fine balance between energy output and using this energy to input into my body for continued healing when I was awake.

I was often guilty of overdoing it. My enthusiasm for feeling good took over and I would extend myself for too long in an activity and then I'd need to recover by doing absolutely nothing. I had overspent my energy and my body was loud and clear about that.

I am finally learning to stop before I reach the point of I've gone too far… again. It's so easy to overextend. We live in a world that values how much you can do and how quickly you can reach a goal. I internalized these values throughout my life and had to be vigilant about catching them when they came up time and time again during my healing.

When I choose rest over being productive, it's a conscious choice. I've learned that conscious rest is actually supporting me in many ways to regain my energy back at a deep physiological level.

I asked my Qigong teacher how I could build up this base of energy in my body that would grow. I often felt, and feel even today, that there are times I'm depleting more than building.

He told me the secret to building up energy that endures with depth is by doing a little bit of Qigong every day and to pay attention as I do a series of movements to how my energy feels. To notice how I feel as I move through the sequence, and when my energy begins to feel strong and my body is totally relaxed, to stay in that place for a few minutes and then finish before any tiredness or strain sets in. So, in essence, stop when my body is feeling at the peak of strength.

I find this incredibly hard to do because that is exactly when I want to keep going and enjoy that feeling of strength, yet there comes a moment when the energy can't support the output anymore, and now I'm in a depletion cycle.

This fine balance of learning how to give my body just the right amount of input so that it can enjoy the full effects of building up strength and then stopping to go into a rest mode is a continuous challenge.

I've been practicing this concept in Qigong, but it can be practiced with everything you do in life. Look for the places you tend to overextend yourself when you keep pushing and think you must do this now or else everything falls apart.

If you can get to sleep easily, this is your blessing. Take full advantage of sleeping. Learning how to rest in a constructive and conscious way is something I think everyone can get better at.

Rest and finding ways to build back up your base of energy becomes more critical when you're healing from an illness.

HOLISTIC HEALING SUPPORT

How did I balance the rhythm of my week? There were so many treatments I was receiving when my program was very active. They included chemotherapy, hyperthermia treatments, chelation infusions, and homeopathic infusions.

Bodywork including massage, cranial-sacral treatments and physiotherapy. I kept up a regular routine of going to the gym when I could and relaxing in the sauna. My days were surprisingly full and keeping track of my calendar was a challenge at times.

I found that it was important for me to have a rhythm to my week so I knew what was coming. I knew that I could expect a certain kind of reaction from the chemotherapy treatments and I set my days up afterwards that would best support getting me back to restoring a better energy flow and clear head.

I created a weekly framework that was within my control and was consistent. Chemotherapy was on Tuesdays and I was accompanied by my friend. I left with a bag of a lesser chemo dose that would last until the next morning when it would be finished. Another friend would take me back to the clinic the next morning to get it unplugged from my port-a-cath.

I was grateful for the ride and company as I was always really tired and wiped out. The first time I tried to undo the port-a-cath on my own at home where the infusion plugged into me I almost fainted. So I opted for going to the clinic for this step.

After I was free of the chemo bag, we'd go for a coffee in town or by the lake depending on the weather. I'd look forward to this weekly visit with my friend and then I would come home and rest for the remainder of that day because I was always very, very tired.

These were the days where I found myself mindfully coloring to music. It was the one thing I could do to pass the time where I was fully engaged in what I was doing. I could take my time and just color ending up with a beautiful mandala or picture. The combination of listening to music, immersing myself in colors, and then having a lovely picture felt very satisfying and healing.

Sometimes I took my coloring with me to appointments or would sit by the lake afterwards. Simply coloring helped to create a peaceful space inside me where my mind and body could be engaged in something creative.

Two days after the chemo infusion, I would go have a hyperthermia treatment. It would be in the morning and take three hours. The point of the hyperthermia is that the heat kills cancer cells and it works synergistically with the chemotherapy. The two together make an even more powerful mix or synergistic treatment in my body against the cancer cells. I was using what energy I did have to continue boosting my body's healing forces.

I did this week after week. It was so powerful and such an incredible experience that I really looked forward to it. Even in my incredibly weakened state it became one of my very beautiful experiences.

The fact that I looked forward to it was great because I was happy and I knew I was doing something good for myself. Even when I would go to the chemotherapy clinic which was a small area I could sit outside in the courtyard on warm days. The nurses were very kind and caring. My friend and I called it the "Chemo Cafe" because they offered us cappuccino, tea, or a cold drink if we liked. Even though I knew what was coming, the whole experience became a relaxing, healing time. I would often put on my headphones and do a meditation and imagine how much good work this cocktail of medicine was doing for me and my body.

Every Thursday I followed up the hyperthermia treatments with a chelation infusion. This infusion was focused on having my body eliminate the no longer active chemotherapy medicine.

I added infusions with homeopathic remedies and extra vitamins to strengthen my immune system and help with my energy levels. This was another feel-good appointment that I looked forward to. I felt so cared for while I was receiving these infusions.

I had weekly massage or cranial sacral treatments and physiotherapy support for my body. This again was a treatment I really looked forward to and was an uplifting intervention to complete my week of caring for my body, mind, and spirit in a way that helped melt away all the challenges from the week.

My week was designed so that by Saturday morning I would wake up feeling really good. I had three days in the week where I had some great energy. I would be riding my bike or out walking and visiting with friends. I had significantly more energy on these three days than the other four days which gave me a big boost of confidence and motivation to begin my next week of treatments again.

I had a rhythm to my week that became like a foundation for me as this was now my life since I wasn't working during the intensive treatment period. Sometimes other appointments were sprinkled on top although these were my core appointments with key people that I felt were an important part of my healing team. I came to call them my dream team because each of them brought their own special flavor of medicine, healing and care to my journey.

Choosing your healthcare team and feeling good about these people is critical. Knowing they believe in you is really important. Their respect for your decisions and how you want to do things is a key component of the healing journey.

This core of specialists has remained with me while many others have joined in the journey for specific treatments and then left. I have always seen each person as another special healer that has come to help me along my journey regardless of what kind of practice they are specialized in. They are my angels meant to help me at a specific time.

Being flexible to adjust the weekly schedule in a way that still supports you getting your rest and feel-good appointments is important. The healing journey is full of surprises and as one course of treatment comes to a completion another one will open up.

And so, the beginning of a new course of treatment begins and with that new specialists that I will see every week along with a new weekly schedule.

I had no idea what was in store for me as I made my way through the radiotherapy and chemo treatment program.

I started my first treatment on 27 April 2017 on a Thursday. I had two days and then a break.

Getting the treatment itself is like driving a big fancy car. I get on a bed that lifts me up under this giant radiation device. I feel like I'm being lifted up towards the heavens and being prepared for a massive blast of focused intensity that lasts in total for six minutes, two minutes of that being the actual radiation zooming in on both sides of my pelvic cavity.

It's deceptively easy because until the side effects start kicking in, it feels like a magical way to eliminate cancer cells. My commute is lovely and serene and takes me about 40 minutes. I drive along the lake of Zürich onto a small car ferry that glides across the lake to Meilen in ten minutes. I enjoy the views of the Alps and the shimmering water.

Once off the ferry, it's an easy lake shore drive for seven minutes to the hospital where I go directly to a separate wing that is only for radiation. This was also the same hospital I had my lung surgeries in and I already had an affinity for this area.

Along with the radiation, I am taking a light dose chemo pill daily to enhance the radiation effects. My oncologist said that some side effects from the chemo pill can be the extreme sensitivity in your fingers and feet. Your skin can become very sensitive to hot and cold, the fingertips turn red and the skin can start peeling away. I didn't have any strong reactions to the infusions earlier so my oncologist thought I'd be fine and basically, not to worry, but to have the awareness this can happen.

The weekly visits I was accustomed to were now longer gaps between visits. My needs and treatment plan was shifting focus towards dealing with the primary tumor in my colorectal area. It was a positive sign I was gaining strength, yet it left a gap in the connections I once had. This becomes another issue, more of an emotional and social longing.

I know I haven't been the only one to feel this shift. Other people who have had intensive treatment have shared with me they felt this emptiness as well. You get used to a rhythm and seeing certain people every week and the energy between the two of you becomes very important. You didn't realize the energy boost you felt until the appointments were not there anymore.

Suddenly you have to begin adapting and adjusting, finding new ways of how to nourish and care for yourself. These new ways became the small transitions that happen as you get better. Everything you'd been working so hard towards is now becoming a reality, however you begin losing people you had come to rely on.

For me, they'd become important people in my life. When I finished with the chemotherapy infusions and believe me, I was happy to stop and finish that stage, I also knew I wasn't going to see my oncologist every week. He was someone that I respected and trusted. I enjoyed our weekly conversations and how he took time to listen and understand my process. I valued his input, and now I was not going to see him so often.

We were making a shift, a conscious change in our relationship with the treatments. I remember wanting to mark this time because I knew from my counseling practice that it's important to mark closures and times of change and transitions in a relationship.

It doesn't matter what kind of relationship it is, if it's a bond of closeness that you've experienced with someone then it's important to acknowledge the change. It was an emotional moment for me, and I'm glad I shared this with my oncologist so I could move forward into the next phase feeling emotionally satisfied.

My treatments were not over by any stretch, I still had surgeries and other types of radiation that I had to do which extended into the following years. It wasn't that he was going anywhere, but the nature of things changed. I was growing, healing and I was changing. I wanted to acknowledge this passage of time.

My radio-oncologist and nurses for radiation had their own stories to tell me about possible side effects from the radiation and what to watch for. It's hard to imagine that any of this will happen to you when you're sitting there feeling just fine and besides, the side effects sound like they're from another world. How could this possibly happen to my body? I listened, although admittedly a little detached from it all, but I wanted to be aware of what's possible should anything come up for me.

Radiation side effects that were within the realm of reality for where my primary tumor was in the rectum were not sounding so desirable if you're a woman. Possibility of the skin burning, peeling, and becoming itchy anywhere within the basin of the pelvic floor area and all the sensitive tissue lining that lives there were all vulnerable to the spillover effects from the radiation. I prayed I would not have to find out what that felt like.

I was free of all these predicted side effects for probably 3.5/4 weeks. Then, suddenly, I started to notice little sensations brewing down under, making it painful to sit and have any pressure on my pelvic floor area. My fingers started getting redder and a little more numb on the tips and then the skin started drying up and cracking. Trying to do simple things like flip open the lid on a jar or do the dishes started to become more difficult and painful.

I am still experiencing these sensations as I type, however typing on my computer is still one thing I can do pain-free. Texting on my phone has become challenging because it hurts my fingers and the screen won't take my fingerprint pressure because I have no fingerprints left. Walking has become more of a chore with painful feet so I've found exercise is limited.

As the days progressed, each day began to take on a slow, unending quality that rolled into a long night and I was getting more and more mentally consumed trying to find ways to deal with the growing discomforts.

Finally, I wrote to my oncologist and said I think I need some pain management. As was the same protocol with my recovery from surgery, once you start the drugs you need to take enough of them to reduce the pain and then keep taking them consistently until the treatment is over and the side effects diminished.

I'm not a fan of drugs however, I have learned to appreciate their place to help one maintain functioning in day-to-day life. Once I started on them, I realized that I had more mental energy and wasn't so dragged down all the time. While they wouldn't take away the pain completely, they significantly reduced it and allowed my mind to be freed up so I wasn't tired all the time.

During my treatments, I also had regular massage and energy work sessions that would significantly reduce my pain and help keep the energy flowing in my body for healing. I also managed to go to Qigong and a light exercise class once a week even though I didn't feel like my body could do anything. To my surprise, once I was there my body was able to do more than I thought it could and I always felt better after the movement and breathing.

As the side effects increased, I found it harder to be powered by my own will and realized how important it is to find movement activities and self-care practices that would support me. Doing something that got me out of the house and into a positive and uplifting atmosphere was very helpful in keeping my mood buoyant.

My radiotherapy treatments were scheduled for 5 weeks – 25x radiation in the general area where the primary tumor was, and a 6th week called a "boost" week, with a range of 5-8x. These visits were specifically to target the area where the tumor was and to eliminate any scavenger cancer cells lurking in the surrounding tissue.

Six weeks would equal thirty visits, meaning 5x of the "boost." Why did the doctor say "it can be 5-8x?" This began to gnaw away at me, and as I felt more and more uncomfortable, I finally asked my doctor, "What's the difference whether it's five or eight?"

I was feeling so grumpy with the continuously building skin irritations, I told him I'm going for 5x as I couldn't imagine bearing anymore. I felt so sure about it.

He said, "We'll talk next week, see how you're doing and you can decide then."

A week passed and we were talking about how many more boosts. He reminded me that the boosts were replacing the operation I didn't get to have because my body had responded so well to all the treatments I'd been doing.

"What we're doing today is not a typical route we normally take so I don't have enough data from previous interventions to tell you if eight makes more of a difference than five."

I began to feel the weight of making this decision get heavier and heavier in my mind and heart. I wanted to make the RIGHT decision to ensure that cancer cells would never come back here again. No doctor was able to give me a definitive answer and I started to really want one. This is where I just wanted someone to tell me what was the optimum number. I assumed eight would be it, as that was the maximum and I was willing to push through and suffer a little longer if it really would make a difference.

This was a turning point for me. Noticing how difficult the decision was to make and that I was looking outward for an answer to stop my inner turmoil.

I knew instinctively that the answer was not to be found outside of myself, that it had to come from within. Decisions like these need to be arrived at with a feeling of peace and a deep inner trust. I lay awake at night, my body clearly agitated by my initial decision of doing all eight boosts. I was not at a peaceful decision yet.

I started listening to my heart and new information started to percolate into my awareness. I realized that maybe just because eight was the maximum didn't mean it was the best or optimum amount for me. It was a random number.

What started to emerge into my awareness was a pattern I played out time and time again. This is one of: hang in there, push through, tough it out, you can do it… ALL.

This type of thinking drove my behavior and my choices. This pattern was all too familiar to me and I could flashback through my life like going through a Rolodex with all the times I operated from this place, all the while making choices governed by my unconscious patterning.

When these shadow sides of yourself are revealed and brought out into the light for further inspection, it simply rocks your world and turns it upside down. At this point, you have a choice, to follow the flow of this new tributary or stick to the regular route.

Healing from cancer has definitely rocked my world and how I take care of my Self, so in my mind and heart, I choose to follow new tributaries.

I chose six boosts and felt complete with that number. I finished on Wednesday, June 14th. While I was very happy to have completed this package of treatments, I was still in the midst of managing intensive self-care for the side effects.

The side effects continued to intensify for a couple of weeks before starting to subside. The body needs time, love, and care to continue healing. Patience.

Be gentle with yourself, you're doing the best you can.

In sharing with my oncologist, who is a caring and attentive listener, I was able to process how hard it's been for me psychologically.

He encouraged me to write about it because, he said, "This is the lowest point in your treatment and it has brought you to such a vulnerable and new way of experiencing your life that you may never be here again."

This was good to hear from him as he has a bigger perspective about what people go through over the course of time with cancer.

This is not anything I would choose to go through, but since I'm here, I have the honor of being present for where it takes me. Despite the hard places I've been visiting, I would not give it up or change it for anything, for the depths I have gone, have brought me into a greater place of loving myself and others that is brighter than I could have ever imagined.

When you are cracked open at your core, vulnerability is waiting for you. Take it by the hand and you are graced with the courage to walk your own true path.

 There is a crack, a crack in everything. That's how the light gets in.

— *LEONARD COHEN*

SOUL ACTIVATION EXERCISE 3: MOVE YOUR BODY!

I hope you're now convinced how important it is to cultivate a congruent mind-body connection in order to support the best outcomes in your cancer journey.

Your next step is to choose the types of exercise & movement that resonate with you.

Then the intention is to do them every day.

I suggest two different forms of exercise. One that emphasizes the integration of mind-body components and another form of exercise where the focus is more on the physical body. Of course, the variety and choice are yours to make.

Choose 3 activities that you find pleasure and enjoyment in.

Discuss an activity/exercise plan with your healthcare team of specialists. This plan is in addition to your cancer treatment plan, not a substitute for it.

If you are in recovery from any kind of treatment then make sure you count your everyday movements into your plan. For example, walking mindfully brings awareness of your breathing, and thoughts focused on each step. This can be considered a form of movement. This reminds you that even though movement/exercise may be more limited at this time, you are still moving your body.

If you have a good level of fitness and are able to do more extensive exercise, work out a program with your healthcare specialists.

Aim to include as many of the points below as possible depending on your physical abilities at this time. You will adjust parts of your plan as you gain strength, mobility, and improved health.

- Low impact exercise
- Repetitious flowing movements
- Weight-bearing movements
- Synchronizing breath & movement
- Mindfulness and meditation
- Energy cultivation with self-massage
- Emphasis on relaxation while moving
- Relaxation techniques using imagery or visualization
- Exercise done with others (if possible)

HOW WILL YOU MOVE YOUR BODY?

1._____

2._____

3._____

Examples of mind-body focused exercises include:

- Qi Gong
- Tai Chi
- Yoga (gentle style: Yin, Hatha)
- Contemplative Dance Movement
- Mindful Walking Meditation

Examples of more active exercise include:

- *Strongly advised under the direction of a Physiotherapist & approved by your doctor*
- Weight-bearing exercises
- Cardio exercise on a gym machine, ie: elliptical, treadmill, or stationary bike
- Specialized exercise machines such as sensorpro
- Any outdoor exercise you enjoy and are still able to manage, ie: walking, running, hiking, skiing, biking

Disclaimer: Please consult your healthcare professional before beginning any wellness exercise program. This information is not intended to diagnose, treat, or be a substitute for professional medical advice.

Go deeper: Continue your healing journey in my online course, Choose Life!

MAKING YOUR HEAVEN CONNECTION

TENDING TO YOUR SOUL GARDEN

Earth is grounding and centering, heaven is uplifting, expansive, and a part of something greater than all of the logistical and physical things that need to be dealt with at this time. Heaven would often become my sanctuary. A place where I went in my meditations, dreams, and sleep.

The idea of a heavenly place would soften me inside. The hard edges would melt and my heart would be more open to listening for what was next. And trust me, there always seemed to be the next step and usually, it was not what I'd be expecting.

I search to feel the ground beneath me. This is something I have done throughout my life, especially in times of perceived adversity. If I could only feel anchored to something that is solid. Although, I am starting to wonder how much of my energy is spent trying to create this elusive and imaginary place.

What am I trying to achieve by drawing lines that will only construct more imaginary walls, ultimately closing me in, when what I really want is a place of openness and unconditional loving energy?

It's not a solid space. It's an energy space.

The emotional, mental, and spiritual bodies make up my heaven connection and I was constantly adjusting the information coming through to me with how my physical body was responding to the treatments.

When I felt the ground beneath me was solid enough and my physical body was making progress, I thought I'd be able to coast for a little while and enjoy a new level of health. I found this was not the case. As soon as my physical body had enough energy and strength a new directive came to me from my heaven connection.

This happened several times, and was like a spiraling into new possibilities that I knew in my heart had to be put on the burning table to be addressed. It was an uncanny kind of feeling that swept through me. There was clarity and fearlessness in the knowing even though my mind knew it would mean huge shifts in my life as I knew it to be.

After my final cyberknife sessions were completed on my lungs, I had a scheduled PET scan that was a routine control check from one done three months earlier. I was warned this would be too soon to see any of the treatment effects and to maybe hold off until mid January. But, I have a revolving calendar of exam checks; one for my liver, one for my lungs, one for my pelvic/rectal area, and one for my whole body.

I agreed to the PET scan because it was a follow-up from three months earlier and as we were in a "critical" period, it was important to keep a close eye on what my body was doing.

What I didn't anticipate would be the spin these results would give me.

It's not uncommon for me to feel some nervous anticipation prior to seeing the doctor after a scan. In Switzerland, I am able to see a doctor who reads the imaging right away and discusses it with me. I then have a follow-up appointment with my oncologist within a day or two of the scan to go over the results and what further options might need to be discussed.

I could tell that the images were tricky to read this time. The doctor said, "There is nothing showing up in the rest of your body, however, your lungs are more difficult to discern because of the recent markers put in."

As expected, the remaining lasered lesions were still showing up.

What I wasn't anticipating was his hesitation around suggesting there may be some other spots surfacing. I could feel the uncertainty and didn't want to proceed with him sensing it would be better to talk to my radio oncologist who knows these images more specifically.

When I felt like my life was on the line, I was willing to do anything. In a way, this made listening to my inner voice and making decisions easier. I had a Bruce Lipton motto that sat in my kitchen and said,

ENERGY = LIFE

Death is Bad Vibes -------------------- **Life is Good Vibes**

This is what I looked at every day and let it permeate my mind. Was my choice producing a good vibe inside my body?

If I got a NO, then I stayed with the process of making a decision until I came to a YES to support my energy for life.

As I diligently tended to my physical body, I was also actively including what I consider the three other vital bodies that needed support for healing.

Before meeting with my oncologist, I found myself being taken over by a swirling vortex of different feelings. The body responds swiftly and speaks directly. It isn't concerned with where I am, whether on a park bench, sitting on the train, or strolling the Christmas market stalls. The body says, "Hello! I'm here, and I feel uncertain, vulnerable, and at the mercy of the unfolding mystery of life."

The mind has to let go of any secret it was holding onto in the way of something it deemed as positive good news and turn towards the sensations coming from the body. Opening up at this moment, while the walls feel like they are crumbling once again, to the flow of information coming from all parts of who I am.

This is the moment of mindfulness, of dropping into the breath, the being with whatever is presenting, regardless of the difficulty, taking away the judgments, and with a soft welcome, opening up to the groundlessness that comes with openness.

When I commit to stepping into this greater flow of life that is always there, a deep ocean of energy and information, I have to drop the idea that there will be a place to plant my feet. Just as I ride a wave in the ocean whether it be swimming, surfing, or paddleboarding, there is surrendering into the momentum of the collective force of the water.

Life does not always deliver what I want. And when this happens, I need to get on the wave and start surfing. Be fluid, dance with the energy of the water, allow it to take me into places I do not know, and be open to unexpected surprises.

How calm and centered can I be in my mind without having giant mood swings from good to bad and everything in between? Am I resilient enough to ride a new wave of news? Can my mind and emotions be flexible enough to weather the uncertainty of the potential storm?

I need to keep meeting uncertainty with stillness. For here, there is a place that is calm, peaceful, and filled with love. It is a place to just simply BE.

After that PET scan, I received information I didn't want. Four more spots or lesions showed up in my lungs. We assumed they were malignant and needed to be dealt with. So it was right back to considering options and next steps.

No one says being with this stuff as it arises is easy.

Welcoming difficult news with open awareness, non-judgment, and even the possibility that there is more to learn here, is always going to be challenging. As my daughter says, "It's like having a bonfire under your ass!"

The heat is high and the moment is NOW to practice this attitude of accepting the news that is coming to me as it is. So I come back to what I just said: be fluid, tap into stillness and imagine that a sense of calm can pervade.

Find that place of peaceful, loving energy and rest there. Breathe. Listen and make choices from your heart space.

Imagine stringing together a series of moments where you just simply are resting in the center of this Beingness. Meditation, Qigong, movement, free-flowing dance, a sport where we are connected to nature are ways to engage the whole body-mind-spirit into this centered place of stillness within the heart-mind.

If I am to have any anchor at all, I would say these activities bring me into a state of mind that offers a space for feeling the quiet still center within my heart mind and the gentle flow of energy that runs through my body.

Contained within the emotional, mental, and spiritual bodies I continue to practice stretching the boundaries of my psychological flexibility and allowing my awareness to rest in the groundlessness of unconditional love.

Each aspect of your heaven connection is a critical piece of the whole spectrum for healing. How can you welcome and work with all these aspects of your being? This includes all the challenging, tough emotions and thoughts that show up, especially when dealing with an illness.

The Guest House
This being human is a guest house.
Every morning a new arrival.
A joy, a depression, a meanness,
some momentary awareness comes
as an unexpected visitor.
Welcome and entertain them all!
Even if they're a crowd of sorrows,
who violently sweep your house
empty of its furniture,
still, treat each guest honorably.
He may be clearing you out

for some new delight.
The dark thought, the shame, the malice,
meet them at the door laughing,
and invite them in.
Be grateful for whoever comes,
because each has been sent
as a guide from beyond.
RUMI

The biggest challenge is to be kind to what is alive at this moment and be open to guidance. Some may call on angels, others a God or Divine energy, an inner listening to the heart, or a connection from being in nature.

However you connect to this wisdom, keep your eyes and heart open. See the path that lights up for you to follow.

ONE: EMOTIONAL BODY

What does it really mean to care for the Self? This continues to be a deepening theme around total healing: respecting self-care like it was the Source of everything, vitally important to well-being. Yet, how does one fit this quality of care into daily life in ways that make a difference to the health & healing of the body, mind, and heart?

Being aware and intentional makes all the difference when it comes to self-care.

POSITIVE HABITS & ROUTINES

If you believed that listening to the voice inside your body, your intuition, was the most important thing you did every day for your health and well-being, would you change the way you make decisions?

For example, would you greet your morning differently? Would the songbird chirp in your ears and the new dawn of the day slowly wake up your eyes? Or are you driven by the buzzing alarm that jolts your body into action mode?

There are many ways to choose how to awaken into a new day. Depending on how you begin your day, can make all the difference as to how the day unfolds.

I am still learning from my early recovery days to wake up slowly and listen for the sounds outside, feel the temperature of the air as it sweeps into my bedroom. My body continues to ask for a rhythm that is very different from the one that dominated my life for over three decades.

Developmentally, life has a rhythm that is hopefully matching our lifestyle and growth as we go through our 20's, 30's, and so on. When an illness shows up the rhythm needs to shift due to new energy levels and possible mobility limitations. This is different for everyone and it's important to listen to your body, energy levels, and personal needs.

This is where self-care comes in. Maybe you're already very good at taking care and giving your body, mind, and spirit what you need. Now you are just making adjustments based on a new situation. Or maybe there's been a level of neglect around taking care of aspects of your Self that could really use some tender self-care.

Cancer has given me the opportunity to slow down in all areas of my life. Not just for a few weeks as in taking a holiday, but for years now. This is one of the ways I believe it's saved me from living a life where I was blind to or maybe refusing to look at the areas of my life that were not working for me.

Rituals I learned during my recoveries have been integrated into my daily life.

My morning ritual has organically grown into an awakening of slowly opening my eyes, laying in bed taking in the sounds around me; the birds singing, water spilling into a small pond, and opening my eyes to the sky. Checking in with my body and saying, "Hello, welcome to a new day."

Once awake, I choose from a combination of reflective practices: meditation, journaling, and/or Qigong or yoga. Sometimes a combination of them all or just one or two.

Imagining the energy flowing from deep in the Earth up through my body out into the sky and the heavens above. My body includes not just my muscles and bones, but the trillions of cells working endlessly to keep me healthy. To continue cultivating unwavering trust in the healing ability of my body and know what it needs for optimum healing.

BREATHING IN, BREATHING OUT

Try it now as you read: allow some of your attention to go to your breathing. Notice how your breath naturally moves in and out of your body. Or maybe you're reading this in a hurry and scanning through the words and your breath follows a similar pattern. Both are fine.

Maybe in this moment of noticing, you decide to make a choice about how you really want to proceed; is it to slow down and focus on your breathing as you read, setting aside everything else going on right now, or is it deciding this isn't the right moment?

We are making choices like this all the time, regardless of what we are doing.

Laying in bed for five or ten minutes before getting up allows me to tune into my body in this quiet, focused way and direct energy that can flow through and around me all day long. My focus lands on a gentle, still place where I am able to fluidly respond to what the day ahead brings me.

This body of mine is still very much in a deep healing mode and I need to continue respecting this and the timing that cellular regeneration takes. I'm learning that it takes a long time for the body to eventually become ill, so while healing can happen right here and now, the physical body still takes time to thoroughly turn itself around. In my case, this has gone from months to years.

PATIENCE MY DEAR, PATIENCE...

Patience is transformed into a newly felt experience. No more am I trying to keep forging ahead, pushing myself to complete to-do lists and get-well expectations. I have scaled back the number of things I do in a day or complete in a week.

Each day, I listen to my body and ask, "What do you need today?" I make sure that many of these needs are tended to throughout the day. I feel how my energy level ebbs and flows as the day proceeds. I notice how I am much more protective of my personal space and choose carefully how I use it.

Some days, I wake up with a strong waterfall of energy pouring through me. Other days, just a trickling stream.

As I cultivate a personal practice of inner-directed activities, I am able to sense my body dropping into a place of waking up energetically; feeling where I am still sleepy or blocked, the sore or tight areas, the emotional tone, scanning through making a non-judgmental inventory.

Spending time focusing on breathing into my whole body from the bottom of my feet up to the top of my head allows me to begin gently connecting to the outer world.

A while back, moving through treatments, my oncologist said to me, "What's more critical for you right now, rather than going away to a rehabilitation center, is to learn how to care for yourself every day, to make each day a Rehab Day."

I was well enough to look after myself, although there was a part of me that fancied being taken care of in the Swiss Alps by a team of professionals. I felt the ring of truth when he said this to me. He was right, it was important that I begin to learn to really take care of my Self. I needed to begin this now.

YOU ARE YOUR OWN EXPERT!

Healing continued for many months after this conversation occurred. I needed to become an expert in my own transformational journey of care. I needed to step into being honest with myself about what my inner voice was telling me. These are the moments where trust, self-compassion, and the power of presence are cultivated.

This is a big challenge for anyone. As a mother, it was a big challenge for me as I noticed how I was conditioned to constantly be caring for my children and family. Over time of caring for others, the ability to care for my Self had slipped away. I didn't even notice how much this had happened to me.

Immediately, my mind goes to thinking that if I am not caring for my children and family 100% then I'm being selfish thinking of myself. An unconscious part of my conditioned beliefs runs on the fact that I think they can't take care of themselves and they are helpless without me.

Of course, babies need your full attention and care. There are very intense times to mothering, and as time goes by, this balance of care and taking responsibility also needs to be adjusted.

Yet, what I noticed as I stepped away from this belief was that my children and husband were very capable of caring for themselves. When I couldn't do it anymore, it gave them the opportunity to grow within themselves.

How was I over-caring for them all these years and short-changing my Self?

The river widened as the years went by and the side of the river where my needs were housed began to be undernourished, while the other side grew with a multitude of flowers and flourished. It's natural for a mother to want to care for the ones she loves however, it's not healthy to do it at the expense of putting herself last or worse, never having the time or energy left to attend to her own needs.

 Stay strong through your pain, grow flowers from it. You have helped me grow flowers out of mine so bloom beautifully, dangerously, loudly, bloom softly. However you need, just bloom.

— RUPI KAUR

A large psychological part of making a shift to greater healing has been recognizing how I had overlooked my own feelings and what my body was calling for. It wasn't that I didn't do things for myself, but I am seeing now that it was what I wasn't doing that was important to change.

THE BODY WHISPERS

This was listening to the quiet voice within that whispers to you in the night. Whispering messages you don't want to hear because it means facing uncomfortable situations. Life is always offering you choices. When you pay attention, you notice the hundreds of choices made every day.

Are these choices supporting your vital life energy or are they draining it away? This is the critical question?

Now I ask myself: does this decision or my response to a situation add to my life force and healing capacity or compromise it and drain it away? How are these choices supporting & empowering my Self, my Soul, my Spirit to heal and live in a deep creative flow with life?

How does my body feel with a decision I make?

When I listen, the answer is clear. It either adds life energy or takes it away. If there is discomfort and discord, then I know I need to re-evaluate my decision.

This kind of clarity has come from dealing with a severe illness where death's presence is waiting at the door. Choices take on the essential vital essence of either this supports my living or it supports my dying. Which do I choose at this moment?

I have no wiggle room to make a choice that isn't in my best living interest anymore. When the body is strong and healthy without an illness pressing in every day making life feel so fragile, there is a false sense of believing that I can spare living with this choice even if it doesn't feel great for me. After all, what harm can it do?

It's easy to rationalize away decisions when there is no immediate life-threatening situation that comes from it.

DIS-EMBODIED OR EMBODIED?

However, what we fail to truly listen to, is the emotional, mental, or spiritual damage that is being created from the decision. Maybe you find yourself feeling agitated, angry, lethargic, or short-tempered?

The body has ways of expressing its discomfort and if not listened to, the emotional and mental bodies then become more disconnected from the physical body. You slowly end up living in a dis-embodied state where your head and heart are not connected.

It is so important and critical to LIVE YOUR LIFE today as if you were to die tomorrow! This is an extreme saying, but find the element of truth within it and make your small, hundred daily choices, with this awareness in mind.

Why go through life watering down the fullness of your Spirit? How deeply satisfying and fulfilling will this be over the long span of your life? When I am about to pass over into the next version of my soul's journey, I do not want to have any regrets.

Ultimately, it is your life to live, and your responsibility to be at PEACE within yourself, to share your LOVE with the others in your life, and remember that when you take care of yourself first, only then are you really able to offer others, the FULLNESS OF YOUR BEING.

When you notice all the things in your life you are tolerating or putting up with then you can decide how you want to respond to them. By taking time to acknowledge all of them from the seemingly insignificant things like procrastinating on a project to the bigger items like dealing with a challenging relationship, you begin to take back your power as you transform those pieces of your life that you're tolerating.

How can you be kind to yourself and foster a sense of inner peace? Is peace even possible within when there is a continuous flood of interventions and appointments to attend to?

I ended up with more visits to the radiation room than I ever expected. Cyberknife treatments were another option to deal with recurring lesions in my lungs after surgery. I had to go for quite a few treatments and during one of these sessions over the summer, my family was able to visit so we enjoyed many lazy summer days together.

Cyberknife feels like the Cadillac of radiation treatment, although it still tires me out. One good sleep does not blast away the deep tiredness. I found the best way to recover was to be outside in the fresh air, moving slowly, with no agenda. Nowhere to go and nothing to do, just be present.

DO NOTHING, FEEL GOOD.

When I created a to-do list for myself of things that needed doing and I tried to get through it, I just couldn't manage it. So, I gave in and let go into noticing when I felt good and what I had energy for. I managed some forest walks, sitting by the lakeside, and sitting at mountain restaurants.

I was feeling good overall. In general, my energy level was improving slowly and my mind felt clear and happy. I knew there were upcoming control exams in September for my pelvic area where the primary tumor was and then again CT and PET scans at the end of September. For now, I was enjoying living free of all the exams and doctor visits except for the Cyberknife treatments.

"Listen inside and do your best to support your whole self for transformative healing."

LOVING YOURSELF VS. HEALING YOURSELF

This Fall, I listened to the Healing Cancer Summit hosted by Kris Carr and the interviews got me thinking about the difference between focusing on healing or just loving myself. When I think about healing my body, it implies there is a split between what's good and what's bad, meaning something is not OK in my body and needs to be fixed.

With an ongoing or long-term health condition, it can start to get tiring, always focusing on healing. Constantly, noticing what's not quite perfect yet and working to bring about change. There's always a feeling of, "My body's still not 100% OK."

By loving yourself, you are saying that "I don't have to be perfect," I can be OK regardless of what's going on, the love is unconditional. There is no judgment about where there might be pain or misguided cells. You simply come back to an inner place of, no matter what is happening, you love your WHOLE BODY.

With prolonged illness learning how to be kind to yourself doesn't go away. It's not something you practice a few times and then say, "Alright, I'm good with this." It's important to make kindness to yourself a continuous practice so that it becomes integrated into your everyday routines and even how you think.

This can be quite challenging to do if you are faced with a cancer diagnosis or another serious illness. How do you come to terms with loving yourself and being kind to yourself when your body is letting you down? This is really hard because all you want to do is get better and of course, there is something that's not well inside you. Is it possible to find peace within while there are imbalances happening?

When you open to the heart energy inside and learn to love yourself as you love a child, a close family member, or a dear friend, you begin to bring self-compassion and loving to your own heartself. As the gap closes between my body is not good enough yet to I love my body however it is, healing and self-love can merge together.

So when you turn towards the cancerous cells and love them, you stop the separation and the battle that's going on inside. You make peace with these cells and bring them into the whole of your being opening up the possibility for transformation to happen.

A cellular transformation that comes through the active focus of loving and a belief that wholeness dissolves any separation, from here healing happens how it needs to.

DOORSTEP OF FORGIVENESS

I arrived on the doorstep of forgiveness in one of my counseling sessions. I cried over the separation I felt inside, longed for my cells to be united in their single-minded focus of: Live, Seek to Bring Health, and then Die and do it all over again the next day.

I am profoundly moved inside when I keep discovering these hidden places of deep disparity inside, working at opposing forces. The best healing for this I find is giving myself self-compassion and forgiveness. Letting go of the way things were, accepting without judging the situation as it is, and finding the pathways of bringing love into all aspects of being, my body, and my cells. Loving myself as I am now. Period. No negotiations.

SCANS, CONTROLS, & BIOPSIES

It was after a routine Endosonography control exam on my rectum in September, the area of the original primary tumor, where the biopsy came back showing some cancerous cells in the tissues.

Shockwaves went through me when I heard this news over the phone.

In the exam room, the pictures had showed a perfectly healthy rectum and the doctor said, "Looks like your disease has stabilized, let's do a colonoscopy in 6 months."

Since I finished the radiation in June 2017, I had been healthy and showing no signs of recurrence, so it was the last thing on my mind when I went in for the control exam. Feeling like I'd been cut off at the knees that afternoon, I had sent myself a chart from a recent talk I'd heard on cancer by Kelly Turner about the 9 common themes of healing. One theme that stood out for me with this news was: Take Charge of Your Health.

TAKE CHARGE OF YOUR HEALTH

Instead of falling victim to this news of: "Why ME, how can this be after all I've been doing, doesn't any of it count?" I found ways to move on with this most recent information.

But first, I cried. Hard. I was an emotional wreck that afternoon and evening.

With the support of others, and finding yet another new place of strength and determination inside myself, I found a way to sleep and come back in the morning with a fresh perspective on my life.

How to Take Charge of My Life? Armed with information from doctor's visits and thoughtful conversations with others, inner listening, I was open to the next direction. After I met with my surgeon, he suggested a less invasive procedure to go in and cut away the misguided cells. This felt right for me and we made a date in November 2018.

As I've said before, each recovery stands on its own terms and this one was no exception. With a less invasive procedure, I thought I would be out after 3 days and that I'd be skipping back into the countryside on Monday. Not so. There were more cells off track than expected, and the doctor wanted me to stay all week on an IV of liquids, antibiotics, and vitamins.

This was to give my body a chance to heal and not have my digestive system working. A journey, it's been once again of unexpected twists and turns and another phase of my healing marathon.

Tomorrow will be 2 years exactly since I had my first lung operation and surgery ever in my life. When I think back to everything that has happened between now and then, it's been a very full life lived with one event after another; something I could never have imagined or made up in my wildest dreams!

Each new twist that appears gives me the opportunity to practice being kind to myself and not to beat myself up once again for going through another treatment.

As crazy as the journey can be, there is always the opportunity to grow and love myself as I am. Not perfectly perfect, yet more aware, more loving, kinder, and filled with a newfound sense of peace.

TWO: MENTAL BODY

Three aspects of developing a deeper relationship with my mind and thoughts are:

1. Compassion towards self and others
2. Mindful awareness of the thoughts running through my mind and relaxing my identification with them by moving into a place of non-judgmental presence
3. Intuition / inner voice - recognizing the difference between how my thoughts filter my intuitive voice and my fearful voice

Compassion towards myself was first tested while I was recovering in the Intensive Care Unit (ICU) after my lung surgeries. I woke up from the anesthesia completely at the mercy of others. My body was feeling heavy all over and I literally could not move a muscle.

Memories, images, and feelings about my ICU stay continue to trickle into my consciousness and I ask myself, how did I manage that experience and be left with such positive feelings?

When your life is stripped down to lying immobile in a bed completely dependent on the care of others, there's only each moment as it passes, thankful to be alive and digging deep to find a place of peace. Embracing self-compassion pulled me through.

I was so grateful for the nurses who tended to my every single need. This was my time to lean back and be held by others who I didn't know. To be open to receiving their expert care and compassion. Their care became a bridge where I learned how to exercise this compassion towards myself.

ICU is 24-hour care, a nurse assigned to you for their 8-hour shift. This means check-ins at least every hour from your nurse and someone who you can trust to make sure everything is going as it should be. They monitor the pain meds, the IV's, and numerous machines that are connected to all of the tubes going into your body.

What really stays with me though are the constant smiles, laughs, the chats we had about what they did in their own time, and the lovely touches of lavender in the bathing water.

The compassion that ICU nurses showed 24/7 amazed me. I could often hear them laughing from their staff area and it always warmed my heart that they were enjoying themselves and happy in their job. Just being around this energy in such an intense environment put my heart at ease.

I thought to myself, I need to be showering myself with this warm, loving, and caring energy. I need to generate this from within so I can keep supporting my body and focusing my thoughts on relaxing in the aftermath of having my lungs exposed.

I was often awake through the night, sometimes because of pain, other times my mind was awake wondering what to do with this experience. It was so intense and hard to make sense of. In these moments, I found myself turning to what I had learned about self-compassion from Kristin Neff's work.

Three components make up self-compassion:

- kindness to self
- sharing common humanity
- mindfulness

I started with common humanity remembering that I am not alone in this experience. Many people have gone before me, had to deal with life-threatening illnesses and recover from big surgeries.

I am not alone in this experience.

Framing my experience in a larger perspective helped me to not feel sorry for myself, as if I'm the only one suffering here.

It helped me tune into a much larger part of life that while I am lying on this bed unable to move, it still is only a small aspect of who I am. I focus on reaching into a more vast and expansive quality of my being.

I remember the words from the Self-Compassion break exercise and say them over in my head like a mantra:

This is a moment of suffering
Suffering is part of life
May I be kind to myself
May I give myself the compassion I need

It's amazing how saying these words over and over again can calm down the mind and fill the body with a mixture of gentleness, love, and acceptance. The willingness to meet and soften to whatever is going on in the moment as the body works hard to readjust its understanding of what just happened to it. Self-compassion gave me the deep internal support I needed to give myself.

As I look back to the beginning of this journey, I have an interesting perspective on time. I can see that my thinking and timeline were way off and I really knew nothing about anything in terms of understanding what it means to be in it for the marathon. My oncologist would tell me in the early days, this is not a sprint Leslie, think of it more in terms of a marathon. Slow, steady, turtle like with unwavering focus.

Thinking of the treatments, recoveries, and changes that my body would adapt to allowed me to relax in my mind about wanting this illness to hurry up and just go away. This wasn't how it necessarily worked. There were no quick fixes so I continued to keep accepting this as I could see that it took time for my body to adjust, heal, and keep going through what I was asking of it.

The summer I was diagnosed, Geoff and I were able to do our Ireland trip and then spend some time back in Switzerland. My idea was to rest and rejuvenate my body and spirit from a tiring second semester of work. Without realizing my exhaustion was a symptom of a much deeper health issue, we managed to do some wonderful biking and hiking.

A visit to Zermatt and a hike down from Gornergrat graced us with a stunning view of the Matterhorn. At the time, I had no idea this would become my mountain to climb.

Looking back since I began treatments in September 2016, I feel like I have climbed 90% of the mountain. I'm close to having an amazing view from the peak, but I'm not there yet. I don't have a 360-degree panorama and that is what I'm looking forward to. A great, wide perspective.

However, it's not helpful to let my desire for a view create impatience for the treatments that still lie ahead. This 10% is just as important as the 90% has been and calls forth a deeper level of mental endurance.

I remember having an enthusiasm to get the chemo treatments started and to finally begin helping my body to get well.

Remembering these early days, my oncologist told me my treatment plan and dealing with cancer will take time. Keep a sustainable pace and maintain the health that the body does have. A motivational quote that my son sent me early on, that rings more true for me today even more so than it did in the beginning is:

"Physical strength will get you to the start line. But mental strength will get you to the finish line."

Eight months in, I have been having the urge to sprint and just be done, completed, cross that finish line!

Since I had the feeling that I had 10% to go, my world view shattered after a couple of meetings with my doctors. Cancer is not something that is simply finished by summiting a mountain peak. The goal may be to reach one peak and be blessed with a greater perspective on life and gain insight into the next steps ahead.

I had unconsciously created false hopes about when this would all end. As the months go by, there is a part of me that just wants it to be over with. It is in these moments that I catch myself wanting to turn away from the frustration or the building irritation inside. I feel myself in a state of disconnection: thoughts flying one way, body shut down. How to transition back to a place of mind-body flow?

I come back to a still place in my body, I stretch and breathe, I meditate, write, talk with others, reflect on all that has happened and where I am at now. I give thanks to my body for working so hard. Eventually, I arrived at the moment of NOW. I feel the mind-body connection and my heart opens to being alive and grateful for all that I have.

It is about the journey and being present with each step of the way, not the destination of having all cancer gone. Fully present, not thinking or wishing ahead for something different, but to be fully immersed in this moment of whatever the treatment may be and where I am on my life path regardless of what my health status is.

I am arriving at a lookout point up on the mountain and taking in the vista from here. Appreciating the distance I have traveled and am ready to put my energy into the next steps that will carry me forward.

At the end of April 2017, I went into the hospital for a liver ablation procedure. No cutting was involved, just a needle into the area in my liver where a small lesion was originally spotted. Although the lesion was no longer visible, the metal marker I had inserted in November was still there marking the spot. I was told this was a low-risk procedure and worth it to heat up and blast out any possible cancer cells that may be still lingering in this area.

What's difficult about getting the tests done is the results may show an area as being clear of cancer compared to the first test, however, I'm told by the specialists that one can never be sure of microscopic, teeny, tiny cancer cells still resting in the area. So to not take any chances, I had this area heat-treated to kill any possible remaining cancer cells. Compared to my lung surgeries, this was pretty easy to endure and I was back home in the evening.

This liver procedure checks off one of the "minor" treatments that I had still needed. I'm grateful to have climbed a little higher up the Matterhorn.

INTUITION / INNER VOICE - LISTENING FOR THIS VOICE AS OPPOSED TO A FEAR-BASED VOICE

I sunk back into the mindful practices I had been doing for a few years and began to practice just allowing the state I was in to be OK. All I had to do was tune in with a body scan and then give myself what I needed. Sometimes it was long hours in bed listening to Deva Premal and Miten mantras, other times it was going for a walk in the forest.

I had to quiet any noise in my head and just listen for what I needed. The truth is, without having a lot of extra energy, this wasn't so hard to do. I didn't have the extra mental energy to have a litany of thoughts streaming through my head. I really had to focus all the energy I had on keeping my body calm and comfortable.

Out of this place of emptiness and calm came the questions to self of what do you need today, what will be best for you, and what will bring you some joy?

At this time, I was very grateful that practicing mindfulness had already become a part of my life. I could feel that my body already knew how to sink into a peaceful, calming place even when the world seemed to be spinning around me.

I realized this is why daily practice is so important. The repetition of the practice trains the body and mind to drop into a connected place and rest there. The more one practices, the easier it gets to arrive in this unified space. So when a challenge arises, then the real work of applying the practice comes into play.

This is where my challenge lies. All the yoga, movement, meditation I had been doing for years, now was really put to the test as I was living through a very complicated life-threatening situation.

I wondered:

"How many ways are there to say goodbye to cells gone crazy?"

What choices have I made to re-establish my body from a shattered temple into an integrated whole?

I have always been a firm believer in digging deep and wide for support whatever the situation may be. I did this as a parent and for those who came to me for counseling. Now I find myself naturally doing it for myself.

Cancer is as individual a healing process as each of us is individually unique.

Health is personal.

It is tied into the very depth of who you are at your core, this is why I believe, it is so vital to deeply believe in the treatments and lifestyle choices you choose.

OPEN YOUR MIND.

LISTEN, RESPOND.

You may find treatments you thought you'd never do you are now open to.

Before cancer, I always thought if I ever got sick I would only do alternative healing treatments. My life was so focused on staying healthy and using natural products. However, when my body was faced with life or death, it was easy for me to accept all that allopathic medicine could offer me.

Today, I am eternally grateful for conventional medicine and have found a way to bring the conventional and alternative/complementary medicines together to create a stronger healing response.

What especially surprised me were the health topics I was noticing that showed up in my email inbox and the thoughts that would pop into my head. Names of healers, books I'd had in the past, email groups I was part of that I no longer followed. A name would come to me out of nowhere, someone I hadn't thought of in years, decades, and then the next day, I'd see the name in one of my emails.

I WAS CONSTANTLY BEING REMINDED TO FOLLOW MY INTUITION, SO I PAID ATTENTION TO THE LITTLE "PINGS" THAT KEPT SHOWING UP.

A couple of significant topics had to do with Energy Psychology and Energy Medicine.

When I was first released from work at the beginning of my journey I found myself with time to circle back to earlier interests. It just so happened that two online courses were being offered in Energy Healing and the Science of Energy Psychology. I thought, why not, sign up and work on it as I can. The online courses gave me a positive focus and something I enjoyed doing when I had the energy.

What are the little pings showing up for you? What are you drawn towards doing? Honor your intuitive pings and see where they take you.

THREE: SPIRITUAL BODY

How is your spiritual wellness blossoming?

When your life is disrupted from the unexpected arrival of cancer, your life goals and plans are also disrupted. The certainty of fulfilling your aspirations that you were looking forward to now has to be laid aside.

This sudden halting of your life as you know it is disheartening, a feeling of life slipping through your hands. How do you consciously keep your life blossoming with the current knowledge of how your body has changed and the new support it needs?

Continuing to support your everyday quality of life is one of the major ways that can keep you feeling alive and joyful. A fulfilling quality of life is made up of a variety of components and three key psychological traits I want to highlight that have no boundaries to how you live your life, your age, or the type of cancer you have are: hope, faith, and resiliency.

Expressing all three of these traits strengthens and supports spiritual wellness.

Having a strong sense of hope, a connection to faith and the ability to bounce back from difficult experiences can support a continued quality of life that naturally embraces the larger spiritual and/or religious aspect of one's life.

How do I talk about the spiritual side of life living through the experience of a life-threatening illness? In fact, I can't think of anything else in my life where I have been continuously brought to my knees praying, again and again, wondering, "What next?" and "How will I choose to rise back up again?"

How do I continue surrendering into the unknown Universal Life Path that is stretched out before me? I think it's impossible for illnesses to not push one towards a deeper spiritual connection that feels greater than the self and yet is deeply connected within the self.

I wonder, do we have control over our lives?

It had been 4 months since my last control scans. I know this scan schedule can bring up a lot of emotions. It's another reminder of how I have to be gentle with myself when my body is speaking to me.

Even when I have been feeling strong, healthy, and fitter than ever with increased mental clarity, going to get a scan brings up waves of emotion that caught me by surprise. It's not so much anxiety as it's more of being absolutely surprised at what surfaces inside me. So for this, the word "Scanprises" came to me; a combination of getting the scan and being surprised at all the thoughts and emotions that run through my mind.

A prolonged illness gives one the opportunity to discover new layers of letting go, each scan bringing a new quality of awareness. As clouds pass by, I watch to see what doors open, which ones close, and how I want to direct the story.

My story unfolds based on what kind of energy my whole body-mind is calling for to keep healing and growing in positive ways.

Breathing, letting energy and stress out through tears, and asking "What do I need right now to bring self-compassion to my body, my heart, my mind?"

I know this is a moment of suffering… and I am not alone.

Leaning into all of my inner resources and using them.

Being kind to myself is amazingly hard when a part of me is thinking, "I should be over this!"

Eventually, this storm passes and I'm left reflecting on what just happened.

Over time, it became clear to me that one really does not have control over life's events.

Life itself as a soul journey is much grander and inclusive of infinite possibilities. Deeper healing in the body occurs when the mind is put to rest and stops trying to control the outcome whether this is acknowledged on a conscious or subconscious level.

Yet, this becomes a paradox.

The mind needs to stop trying to solve all the problems, fix everything, and look for a way out. I don't want to neglect the mind as it has its place however, how can it best be utilized to support and enhance healing?

I worked through Louise Hay's 21-day mirror course on self-love and found it incredibly powerful and inspiring. Doing such direct and loving affirmations every day has a way of shifting thoughts into a source of such healing energy for the body. This is how Louise Hay said she healed her own experience with cancer, by eventually becoming a vessel of self-love.

Doing the mirror course was like taking a flashlight and shining it in all the nooks and crannies of my body, mind, and heart to find the tiny tucked away places that were still harboring resentment, anger, sadness, or whatever unresolved emotion was still hanging around.

One of the ways I was able to transform these stuck emotions was to acknowledge them and then allow them to change through forgiveness and unconditional love by using daily affirmations.

The goal is not to be this perfect human being with nothing going on inside, but rather to accept unconditionally whatever does show up and be willing to let go and move on.

Using affirmations was something I could do myself and helped build up resiliency and connect my inner sense of being to an energy greater than myself. I noticed my faith was expanding and deepening inside me at the same time.

I started working through the Biology of Belief and science of Epigenetics online course with Dr. Bruce Lipton. I am having a lot of "aha!" moments about how cells live and healing occurs. Through his talks, I am becoming a cell to understand how this tiny microcosm is a complete reflection of my whole body.

From the time of my diagnosis in August 2016 until now, I have stayed away from asking myself the question, "why me?" I knew it wouldn't be helpful in terms of taking away this illness. I was a person who valued my health since I was young. Never did I imagine that I would be susceptible to cells that would mutate into cancerous ones.

It's been a process of re-learning how to listen to my body and trust my inner voice that is in harmony with my heart and mind to really grasp how influential my thoughts are on my cells.

 The moment you change your perception is the moment you rewrite the chemistry of your body.

— BRUCE LIPTON

Spiritual blossoming and staying grounded in the physical realm are intertwined and this makes it tricky to separate the two. Each aspect influences the other. I spent time reading, researching, and gathering information as this was an important and natural step to take when I was trying to decide how to move forward as I dealt with this massive imbalance in my body.

However, I also found it incredibly overwhelming because there was a part of me that just wants to get the recipe for success to health and begin implementing it. There are conventional treatments and then there are all the complementary approaches that are as broad and plentiful as an alpine meadow in bloom. They all look like great options, but which ones are best for me?

What is the combination that will bring me back to my healthy center of being?

This is the question that calls for a deep dive down into the very core of your existence.

Whether you call that center Spirit, God, Creator, Soul, or another name you identify with, it's critical that you connect with this place inside yourself. It is the opening to your inner voice or intuition and here is where you will uncover your personal path.

During this "time off," I have read in different places that illness is a time to reset your Self, your Body, your Spirit. It is the body's way of saying, "You're not listening to me so I'm making you STOP your life and pay attention!"

For this, I am grateful.

It's an opportunity to bring the spiritual and physical aspects of life into a seamless alignment.

One way of coming into a seamless alignment is by believing in your Self. The way you focus your mind on your thoughts and what you believe is a critical piece in how you can have a major influence on your diagnosis and improve the quality of your daily life regardless of what's happening in the body.

Choosing to practice daily mindful and contemplative activities can create a positive, life affirming energy in your body and directly signal this message to your cells.

ARISE

Every cell in your body is created to rise to challenges.

Your life is meant to confront everything that holds you captive.

— RUMI

 You are liberated through the hope in your heart.

You shall rise like the sun and begin anew.

Rise up, it is your time.

— ALANA FAIRCHILD

Connected between these two powerful forces of energy: Heaven and Earth, I am a conduit for Great Love energy to flow through me.

In this flow of energy, I can give and receive in limitless ways. It is not constrained to a finite amount. This is the wonder of it.

I am not drawing on my own energy and what reserves I can parcel out to others, nor do I have to worry that I am pulling out energy from others and draining them. I am freed up to give and receive more.

Bernie Seigel writes about his experience as a surgeon and when in despair of feeling like he's not doing enough for his patients he goes to sit with his sickest patient. "I guarantee that your patients will heal you in the time that you are sitting there, by their strength, their courage, and the fact that they don't ask you for a cure but are healed by your care."

I think a big piece of curing happens from the care. If the focus is only about curing, all of the deep caring and love gets overlooked and this is where healing power lies and is unleashed. Siegel goes on to say that "the healing I have done as a doctor has always come back to me tenfold. So who is the healer, who is the healed?"[1]

I have been shown this inner place of opening up to the energy of Great Love, an unconditional energy of love that has no boundaries and is forever moving in a natural ebb and flow. I now trust to just rest in this dynamic exchange of energy.

Saki Santorelli in his poetic way reflects what I am struggling to find words to express. When "we touch the brokenness and wholeness of being---our humanity---with less struggle, more ownership, allowing ourselves to be more fully with what is" we arrive in the moment of our wholeness.[2]

This journey has become my school of life, my major in diving into a deeper practice of mindful and compassionate meditation while merging into wholeness embodying a Greater Love, one that is unconditional without any separation between you and me, practitioner and patient, just a body of love that flows freely. This ocean of love holds vast potential for integration and an opportunity for mutual transformation.

Patiently and silently the stillness of love waits for my heart to unfold.

Cultivating hope, faith, and resiliency becomes a beautiful combination of how you can support your own spiritual blossoming. This happens in so many unexpected ways when you keep the door open to greater possibilities.

I have stepped through this heavenly door of what feels like otherworldly adventures many times and this particular time was no exception to the surprises that lay waiting for me to embrace.

COME DANCE WITH ME

Through the eye of intention and focus, each small spot brings a story, patiently waiting to be uncovered. Gently placed in the lobes of the lungs, they surface and show their presence. While it feels like they are relentless in their determination to keep coming forward, I am relieved that they are willing to show up and be seen. They offer an invitation to dig deeper, to explore and uncover the mysterious worlds that lie within.

At first, there is some hesitation in my mind, like being part of a slow dance that I am being dragged into, I don't know the steps and I'm off balance. I dance, but I'm ready for the song to be over. They are not. The music keeps on playing, holding me close in this unfamiliar territory.

I notice that by staying close, I can listen for the rhythm. Find the next steps. I have met this music before adjusting my dance, trying a new flow of movement. Sometimes, the steps are familiar, yet always new patterns are emerging.

Illness begins to take form when there are persistent energetic blocks starting in the outer energy bodies and then eventually making way into the physical body. Releasing emotional blocks that have been unconsciously long held in the body, is a powerful step to take towards total healing. Always, the option to evolve in your growth is a choice and there is never one way to do this.

Perhaps a new meditation on releasing limiting beliefs about self-healing or exploring how it's possible to have the body heal within a sense of altered time where it is not bound by our linear world, making total healing possible right here and now.

I have combined the healing of Theta meditation and distance healing with the intense focus of radiation on both my primary tumor in the rectum and post lesions in my lungs after surgery. Week after week of fine tuning this focus until it was so laser sharp there was no room left for doubt about whether it was going to work or not. It was working and with each treatment and day that passed, my body slowly began to grow itself anew.

Ten months later, I am still being called to dance with my lung spots. This time, it is not with radiation, but with the radiating brilliance of my heart. It is time to shine the light on the dance floor again where steps have not yet met the open space.

The journey through cancer cannot be taken alone. There are so many unknown twists and surprises along the way, that a call for different specialists and support people is needed as new situations present themselves.

I had been looking for a therapist for a while and was waiting for the right one to show up. I knew I wanted my body to lead this dance and have someone support me. Eventually, months later, at just the right time, I found her. She came with experiences that fit my needs perfectly and I knew that once again, my angels had delivered me to another special person to help me along my journey.

It came to me one day that maybe I could learn more about these four spots from the Medicine Wheel and the Four Directions. I took this little hunch into my counseling session and after talking about the Directions and my attitude towards death, I surprisingly found myself sharing the story about how my Dad died and what was going on in my life at that time. Out of nowhere, the body introduces a new dance.

We make connections to the lungs and grieving that I had made before and now find myself coming back to again. My Dad died in the water, suffocating from a lack of air. The themes that endure through my healing are Birthing and Breathing; the creativity of new life, the second chances that come with being re-born, and the fullness of life when one is breathing with their whole body and soul.

I have been convinced over and over through my experiences with this illness, that the body holds all, forever and ever. There is no trauma, too small or big, that goes unchecked by the body. How illness manifests is a completely personal matter, this I know. And this is why treating an illness is so uniquely tailored to the individual.

Each person has their own set of life experiences and also inherited traits that are passed down into their soul being. In order to fully and completely heal you need to get out on the dance floor and learn new steps, take risks, and set yourself free from the dances that no longer fit for you.

I thought I had grieved my Dad's passing 24 years ago, yet I still found places inside me where I was in an energetic hold with him and now it was time to truly set him free. To let his Spirit go so that we could share a higher love and connection, where the love could unconditionally flow and be free to show me a new dance.

There are as many ways to heal as there are ways to dance. **What dance is your body calling for?**

Don't let fear of the unknown hold you back. Accept the invitation to the open space and see what happens.

With hope in your heart and deepening faith in spirit, take that step beyond your comfort zone and allow a path to unfold that is beyond your imagination. Even with bumps along the way, you will bounce back with a newfound feeling of buoyancy and inner strength that will carry you through the most unexpected times delivering you into new life experiences.

SOUL ACTIVATION EXERCISE 4:
TOLERATIONS & TRANSFORMATIONS

It's time now to reflect on the areas of your life that are not fitting for you anymore. Where are you tolerating things that you'd like to let go of?

Dive into the 3rd soul activation exercise and watch areas of your life transform!

First, identify the things you are tolerating in your life and decide how to address them.

Tolerating something means that you are putting up with a behavior either in yourself, from someone else, or a situation you turn a blind eye to. It can be in any area of your life. It is usually something small enough to be an annoyance, but not big enough to take action on.

However, what happens over time are these little things begin to build up, and soon you don't realize the total impact all these tolerations are taking on your energy. You slowly become accustomed to them and unconsciously adjust your expectations.

You may feel irritated, bothered, or frustrated about something, yet you submit to it and so it remains in your life, grating away at your energy, happiness, and quality of life.

Now is the time to expose all of the things you've been tolerating.

Without judgment, create a list for yourself of 20 items, like a stream of consciousness pouring out of you. Once you have your list, sit with it for a day or two and then come back with an open mind and choose which tolerations you want to begin transforming.

EXAMPLES OF TOLERATIONS: cluttered areas in your home and/or at work, broken things that just never get fixed, unfinished projects sitting on a shelf, unresolved discussions with co-workers, small (or big) disagreements that linger with partner/spouse that goes undiscussed, not feeling satisfied with decisions affecting your health treatments, feelings of not being heard or taken seriously

Tolerations list: begin with 20 items. Hint: no toleration is too small to put on the list. (create two columns 10 lines each numbered)

Congratulations! You can move on to part 2 of the exercise.

TRANSFORMATIONS

Now that you have your list you can decide how you want to transform each toleration.

You will find that some are relatively easy to face such as cleaning up a cluttered room in your house. You may even ask someone to help you do it or delegate the task to a specific person. Not everything needs to be done alone by you.

Certain items will need to be put on hold until others are dealt with. You will know which ones these are. Listen to your inner voice and be honest with yourself. The rest will follow naturally.

The tolerations that create a physical reaction in your body when you read them are the ones that probably need immediate attention and once addressed will have a positive ripple effect on your energy level.

TRANSFORM YOUR ENERGY INTO HEALING ENERGY

As you close the gap between what you've been tolerating in your life and how you want to be spending your time as you heal, new energy will be freed up. This energy can now be used towards your healing.

When you eliminate or shift how you handle the situations you've been putting up with, don't be surprised if feelings of relief, peace, calm, and happiness begin to flood through your whole self.

Trust the process. You may not see the path ahead, yet each step feels as if you are moving into harmony with your body, mind, and spirit.

When you name what it is you've been tolerating you give yourself the gift of transforming it and creating the life you want to live. It is a choice point. Louise Hay said, "The point of power is in the present moment."

How do you feel when you take charge of releasing the things you've been tolerating? Watch for feelings of confidence, courage, and empowerment to grow within you.

Go deeper: Continue your healing journey in my online course, Choose Life!

PART III
EMERGENCE

THE HEALING SPIRAL

THREE PATHWAYS

Depending on where you are along your healing journey, there are always possibilities for new directions to emerge. I see this as a spiraling process based on your current needs. Three pathways that became distinct for me while I was healing through treatments and afterward as I slowly found the openings into a new way of living were:

- Making my home a healing sanctuary
- Noticing how I wanted to manifest a new way of being in the world that directly resonated from my soul energy
- Being willing to address the important relationships in my life and make adjustments

HOME AS A HEALING SANCTUARY

My journey has been long and given me the time to reassess how my home is either supporting me or taking away energy from me. I started becoming very aware of how my energy levels felt when I was at home.

I began to hear that whispering voice inside me say, "You need a place of your own to heal."

At first, I didn't want to hear this because it would mean big changes, so I ignored it. But the voice didn't go away. Every day I heard, "You need your own place." A place where there is no other competing energy and all your energy can be focused on healing. It became obvious to me that this was the next step I needed to move forward on even though I felt scared to address it.

I talked to my husband about this need that I was having, and although it was a hard idea to accept, eventually we came to an agreement that I would move out somewhere temporarily to give myself the healing space I felt I so desperately needed. We'd been living together for 25 years, so this was not an insignificant shift.

I didn't know where I was going to go and I didn't have the energy to worry about that next step. It took all my energy to just take one step at a time and then be open to what would be revealed to me. Trust and surrender were the pillars holding me upright.

Two days later, after sharing this news with a close friend, I was offered a furnished home to stay in for as long as I needed. I saw this offer as a gift from heaven and a signal that I was on the right path.

This was a big step towards creating a healing sanctuary where I could collect all my energy towards healing my physical body and the other areas of my life.

How have you made your home a sanctuary for yourself? Is it a space that when you enter you can truly relax?

You don't look around and see all the work that needs to be done instead, you look around and see that there are corners of beauty and areas radiating stillness and peace. Maybe there's flowers in a vase by a window and plants thriving. There's an outdoor area that you enjoy relaxing in and what about some twinkle lights that add an extra sparkle to the evening sky.

Any piles of paper, clothes or dishes, or whatever it may be, that can have a tendency to clutter up space have been dealt with. This isn't to say that my home is always clean and perfect, but I recognize that keeping my place emanating a feeling of beauty and tranquility is important.

What can I do to be mindful of encouraging more of this kind of energy in my home? For example, I may take one week of the month, and deal with all those piles of paper that have filled up on my desk, pay all the bills, reconcile my financial books, tidy it all up, and put it away. I may do the house cleaning or I may arrange for someone to come in and help me with that. I don't have to do it all alone.

As women, I think the tendency is to take care of all the household tasks alone and then we tire ourselves out afterward. My new motto is to do what I'm comfortably able to do and let go of the rest, then ask for help with the remainder of things I'd like done.

So what does your home sanctuary look and feel like for you? What are the small things that you can do that will raise the vibration and increase the positive energy in your home?

Is your home or a space in your home a place where you can feel relaxed and at peace, where you can sit down on the sofa or in a comfy chair and just enjoy the atmosphere? If children are at home, then find a quiet place for yourself and set your boundary around it. Teach others to respect your space.

Are you able to let go of thoughts of I should get up and do this or that? If you're not able to, then you're not really enjoying your space. Your mind is busy thinking about the next thing to do instead of just being present and being able to let your body really relax into enjoying a beautiful environment.

Creating a serene and aesthetically pleasing environment is important for your healing. Honor how your life is needing to make readjustments. Trust that you know what to do and surrender to taking a step forward.

VOCATION

Your soul evolution is something you've been fostering for a long time now. As you've been developing your earth and heaven connection you've simultaneously been connecting more deeply to your inner voice. What is your word for this inner wisdom? Intuition, gut reaction, an inner knowing without words, spirit, whatever it is that resonates for you, name it and go with it.

I often felt like I lived a parallel life between my career and having a vocation. I knew I was in the general zone of where career and vocation could intersect however, I didn't feel at one or in complete alignment with this inner calling that had a way of tugging on me. I was in parallel tracks, traveling closely together but not completely in sync.

What I have come to discover around my soul's calling is that beyond any doing of a specific activity, it is more about being in an energy. I was always looking outside myself for how I needed to be doing things differently, but what I've found is that when I turn my eyes inward and open my heart, it is about fully embracing the unconditional loving energy that lives within me and not being afraid to share it regardless of what I'm doing.

My soul's calling is invisible. It's not anything that I can see. It is something I feel and share through the choices and actions I decide upon doing. First, it is about being and then the doing naturally follows. This is when I feel aligned, whole, and free inside.

The challenging part of tuning into your soul in this way is that you're not going to see the whole picture of what's unfolding before you. That's just how this works. It seems that you have to take a step, a leap of faith, and continue to keep following your inner voice from nudges that you hear or feel even if you don't totally understand it or can't make logical sense of it.

You trust and release control of the mind wanting to know where you're going and what the outcome is going to be. You say to yourself, "I believe in you, I'm going to make this next move." When you make decisions from this place inside your heart in a place of being in your soul energy, you are now expressing your vocation.

That's you, listening to your soul's calling, taking messages, and responding. And sometimes this takes a while for you to really get a grip on it because it's scary. Oftentimes, it can mean changes in your comfy world.

It can be that the structures you have in place that are being called into question now are not fully serving you. If you honestly take a look at them, letting them go can be the next best thing to do and what will ultimately lead to greater healing and living a more fulfilling quality of life.

When this level of integration aligns, synchronicity happens. The separation that has been present between your mind, body, heart, and soul naturally melts away. Fearful states are replaced with unconditional loving energy. Fear cannot exist where there is love.

Extending this feeling of connectedness within yourself, you look around your environment at the sky, at nature, and feel an immediate oneness. A natural merging with earth and heaven is available for you. You are a part of the Universe and the Universe is a part of you.

Breathe in this beautiful experience.

You are fulfilling your soul's purpose. It's that simple. It's that easy. You don't have to go outside yourself looking for anything. Everything you need is within you.

Any fears you have around not fulfilling your soul's purpose or doubting that you don't know what you're doing and are worried that you might die before you get there show you that you're focusing on a destination. Your soul does not have an endpoint, it continues to evolve through lifetimes. If fear is present, come back to your breathing and use your body as an anchor.

Go outside and look at nature, let go of the thoughts circulating through your mind and allow the present moment to be what fills up your body and mind. Acknowledge that you are living here now, your heart is beating and there is so much vitality in your body, regardless of what things might not be perfect physiologically or psychologically. When the separation disappears so does the fear. Now allow loving energy to flow through your body.

A powerful practice that I continue to deepen in is the meditative movements of Qigong. I have been practicing the Sheng Zhen style of Qigong that is transmitted by Master Li Junfeng and the philosophy this style embraces. When I settle into my body and breathe more deeply and fully into my organs and muscles there is a quality of trust and safety within myself.

My teacher, Tsultim Namdak shares with me how "Qigong practice is supported by the breathing technique and visualization. The best way to take a breath is, soft, slow, long, and deep.

Doing the movements with a relaxed chest during inhalation helps you to channel Qi easily into the abdomen. Over time you will discover an even deeper level of breathing behind this technique."

Practicing Qigong supports my whole body, mind, and spirit to be in the present moment and opens up a gateway into my soul's expression.

RELATIONSHIPS

When life surprises you with a life-threatening illness or a tragic event that just collapses the bottom out from under you, how do you respond emotionally?

One way of responding can be to immediately think that you are the only one suffering from this difficult situation and retract from life or another way to respond is to reach out for support and find meaningful relationships in your family and community.

My cancer diagnosis shook the ground beneath me and all the connections I had in my life. With every connection there was an opportunity to reset or reorganize and almost without realizing what was happening, a re-leveling of relationships started happening.

This was one of the ways cancer continued to offer me an opportunity to open up more windows for air to circulate and give me a fresh perspective.

I noticed circles of relationships around me. I was a high school counselor at the time and immediately there were colleagues who came forward wanting to help and visit me in the hospital. Parents and students expressed their support. I wasn't invincible and now it was my turn for receiving care and support.

Many people poured out their hearts in ways that completely surprised and touched me deeply. Others slipped away. All of it was perfectly fitting. I was uplifted by the generous energy that people showered me with. We shared warm, nourishing, and beautiful times together. These moments of connection were so important for me and they sprang out of nowhere.

While these circles have continued to ebb and flow over the years, my inner circle of the people who have been with me the longest through my life was of course my family and some close friends from my childhood. The biggest shifts and most dramatic changes came within the traditional nuclear family circle I had built with my husband of twenty-five years.

Relationships became a vital area of my life to look at and facing the main primary relationship with my husband was a key partnership that could not be overlooked. So many of my patterns and ways of expressing myself were tied up in how we were together and how I was as a mother.

Inner nudges have a way of shining a light in places where I had been previously blind to, this one was no exception. The patterns that had been built over the years of being together needed to be reassessed.

The metaphor that kept surfacing was a burning table, and so it came to me that this primary relationship in my life had to take the heat of this table, just like everything else in my life had. The burning table was symbolic of getting it all out in the open, everything that had been swept under the carpet over the years and to see what was left. What was no longer serving me and our relationship and letting it go as well as seeing what was unburnable that still held value and love for me?

This was really difficult and challenging to do yet I knew in my heart it was a necessary step of this healing journey I was on. I also knew that what was healing for me had the potential to bring healing to the others involved.

When I was listening to my inner voice, and it was telling me I needed space to heal, and time to be alone, I also needed time to reassess this relationship. It meant taking a huge risk and letting go of my life as I had known it for a quarter of a century. I clearly saw it as part of my soul's evolution and as with other areas of my life, a shift was needed. There was no life raft for me.

This was a completely unexpected turn. Even I didn't see it coming until it was upon me. Nobody saw it coming, least of all my kids. This wasn't just about me having cancer anymore, it was now directly affecting my family and our family dynamic we had all come to know over the last 25 years.

As I shared this new development with my kids I was in awe of how well they understood what I needed and that I was making this decision for me even though I knew it would be hard for them to integrate these shifts into their lives.

I trusted they had the inner resources to process this change and to ask for any support they needed. I realized I can't make decisions to protect them from facing challenging situations and this now applied to our family dynamic. I believed in them and their emotional maturity to embrace the new changes that were coming.

The unburnable nuggets that remained from the burning table continue to be nurtured by coming together for family gatherings and sharing holiday times. Twenty-five years of raising children together is an experience close to my heart and one I am grateful for. It was the relationship patterns that had to shift.

Our family dynamic changed to living in our own homes, being separated, yet still maintaining a close bond within our family and the connections we had fostered and nurtured together over a quarter-century. This, I am so appreciative of, and the space created has allowed for deeper relationships to develop with each of our children.

I see our family learning how to keep spiraling upward into a new evolution of sharing times together, not giving in to the thought of another failed marriage that didn't make it. This marriage needed the windows opened with fresh air blowing through to help us see how we can still share time together in new and unconditionally loving ways.

"We are here to gently support each other and reach deep inside to feel the places where everything melts away and only love is present."

SOUL ACTIVATION EXERCISE 5: CREATE YOUR OWN INTEGRATIVE LIFESTYLE HEALING PLAN

Now it's time to put everything you've been doing into your Integrative Lifestyle Healing Plan.

This is a beautiful way to support loving your body and nurturing your experiences. Here you can track everything you're doing in all the areas of your life and make adjustments as you go. You'll be amazed when you start filling in the chart and see everything that you've been doing.

Be proud of yourself. You are facing the hardest challenges of your life.

You are an incredible human being living a soulful journey.

Now it's your turn to see all that you're doing with your integrative lifestyle healing plan.

Begin where you are and write down everything you're doing now in my suggested chart or feel free to create your own.

You can also write down the things you'd like to do in the near future that you are not able to do yet.

This is a work in progress, it's a process, not an end in itself. Life is fluid and ever-changing.

I've created space in the chart for you to acknowledge how you're feeling and who you are having social visits with and when. Energy permitting, it's important to have ongoing meaningful social connections.

Here are some examples to get you started. They are intended to nudge your awareness of ALL that you are doing (in case of brain fog) and to offer the possibility of other treatments you may not have thought of and want to investigate for yourself. My examples are by no means a complete list of what's available. Do your research and be willing to have an open mind.

HEALING HAPPENS IN ALL WAYS

Examples of treatments/protocols/interventions: chemotherapy, radiation, surgery, immunotherapy, CT/MRI/PET scans, anti-cancer integrative supplement program, hyperthermia, homeopathic/herbal/chelation infusions, ozone therapy, somatic-based therapies such as craniosacral, massage, physiotherapy, energy healing/balancing, reiki, EFT/tapping, any form of counseling therapies / personal-lifestyle coaching, aromatherapy, hormone therapy, nutritional program

. . .

Examples of daily movement & exercise: walking around your living space whether a hospital or home, being able to dress/shower yourself, being able to do some cooking & light cleaning of your environment, rehab movement program, walking, using equipment at a gym, attending an exercise and/or yoga/pilates class, outdoor activities you like such as bike riding, running, hiking, swimming, stand up paddleboarding, sailing, gardening, horseback riding, skiing, snowshoeing. Activities vary depending on the season. Think ahead to what you'd like to be doing in the next season & when you're feeling ready for it.

Examples of contemplative & restorative practices: mindfulness meditation or a style you resonate with, restorative yoga, qi gong, tai chi, sauna/steam, journal writing, reading, visualization exercises, mindful coloring, drawing/painting, dancing/authentic movement

Activity (list your activity below)	Monday	Tuesday	Wednesday	Thursday	Friday	Saturday (free day)	Sunday
Chemotherapy		9 - 11am					
Massage	2 - 3pm						
Physiotherapy					11 - 11:30am		
Complementary Treatment				3 - 4pm			
Walk or other exercise	9 - 9:45am		9 - 9:45am		9 - 9:45am		10 - 11am
Qigong			1 - 1:30pm			10:30 - 11:15pm	
Meditation / Music	8 - 8:30am	12pm onwards as needed	8 - 8:30am		8 - 8:30am		8 - 8:30am
Yoga / Stretching				10 - 11am			10 - 11am
Coaching Support			2 - 3pm				
How do I feel today?	Relaxed Happy Tender	Tired Worn Out Fragile	Supported Connected Optimistic	Inspired Strong Confident	Overwhelmed Unhappy Tired	Relaxed Spontaneous Loving	Worried Uneasy Frustrated
Who did I visit with?	Friend	Family	Phone Call Visit	Friend	Friend	Family	Family

Here is an example of what a chart can look like. Fill in your own weekly plan by downloading a special PDF at: **lesliepeake.com/healingbonuses**

Disclaimer: Please consult your healthcare professional before beginning any wellness program. This information is not intended to diagnose, treat, or be a substitute for professional medical advice.

Feel free to use the feeling word list chart below to help best describe how you're feeling today.

Feelings Word List

Protective Emotions						Connective Emotions		
Anger	**Fear**	**Panic**	**Sadness**	**Weak Feelings**	**Seeking/Engaging with Creation**	**Caring Connection**	**Playful Connection**	**Sensual Connection**
annoyed	uneasy	mixed up	disappointed	*Physical Fatigue*	curious	helpful	relaxed	flirtatious
agitated	tense	unsure	low	thirsty	clever	secure	glad	affectionate
fed up	nervous	uncomfortable	down	hungry	inquisitive	attentive	light-hearted	tender
frustrated	insecure	troubled	gloomy	tired	motivated	considerate	amused	cuddly
irritated	worried	insecure	disturbed	run-down	stimulated	friendly	cheerful	frisky
mad	afraid	disoriented	unhappy	worn out	active	kind	comical	romantic
resentful	frightened	stunned	hurt	sore	energetic	understanding	silly	physical
	intimidated	shocked	awful	powerless	constructive	giving	happy	turned on
	fearful	anxious	distressed	shaky	productive	supportive	optimistic	amorous
	anxious	stuck	hopeless	sick	creative	connected	alive	desirous
	panicky	lost	miserable	impotent	eager	tender	delighted	aroused
		trapped	heartbroken	ill	bold	loving	giggly	stimulated
		desperate	depressed	frail	artistic	nurturing	spontaneous	passionate
		helpless		lifeless	fascinated	joined	imaginative	
				exhausted	confident	attached	joyful	
				stressed	focused		spirited	
				fragile	determined		energized	
				vulnerable	inspired		excited	
				insecure	ambitious		bouncy	
				discouraged			lively	
				overwhelmed			ecstatic	
Leslie Peake Counseling 2022				*Emotional Fatigue*				

Go deeper: Continue your healing journey in my online course, Choose Life!

CONCLUSION: FULL CIRCLE

YOU ARE ENOUGH

After traveling to the darkest depths of my soul and then coming into the light of day with new levels of awareness and insights, I find myself experiencing a new way of living. A place where it's perfectly acceptable to be exactly as I am and to feel and know in my heart that I am enough.

While there is no one definitive answer on how to heal or get rid of your cancer, I can say that the healing journey is a rich and transformative one. Staying focused in this way is a healthy approach to remaining in the present with all that is happening without rushing to a final destination.

A life-threatening cancer diagnosis is not a quickly resolved event that suddenly shows up and then ends. It is a process and an ongoing journey that is showing you new ways to embrace your life.

To live in the present moment, connected to all of life, and having new inner resources is a massive step in opening up to all that life brings to you. Embracing each day with reverence, gratitude, and the joy of being alive is empowering and can set you free inside.

Look inside yourself, ask questions and listen for your next steps. Even with meditation, I can fool myself into thinking I'm looking inward, but I'm really wanting to know where I can find the answers outside of myself. Can I trust that sitting with the energy of simply BEING with an open heart center and connecting to something greater than myself is enough?

This is a continual challenge that life brings me and I can say that yes this is enough. Trusting this quiet beingness where I am feeling the energy of my soul on fire just waiting to be shared with the world is all there is.

You can face the biggest challenge of your life when you open your heart to the healing power that lives at the very core of your being.

Live each day to its fullest; your body is here for a finite amount of time, but your soul is not. Love your body up fiercely every day and let the rest of life's pieces find their own natural reorganization. You are enough and you always have been.

ABOUT THE AUTHOR

Leslie Peake, M.Ed is a life coach and holistic counselor. She synergizes the best of science and natural healing methods to support people in their healing process through cancer by using life-extending practices into a personalized and integrative approach. She's sharing her healing recipe with the world.

Leslie began her investigation into integrative medicine in response to her stage IV cancer diagnosis. She immediately implemented vital practices into her life and discovered how they positively influenced her quality of life; living long past a potentially deadly diagnosis.

Join Leslie through group or individual sessions, or continue your journey with her online course - Choose Life!

https://linktr.ee/lesliepeake

 Leslie invites you to contact her and share your story at: www. lesliepeake.com Or send her an email: leslieapeake@gmail.com

THANK YOU

PLEASE LEAVE A REVIEW!

Amazon.com/review/create-review?&asin=B09VJY7GPB

By leaving a review, you make my book more visible on amazon which will help more people find it and ultimately support them along their journey. Let others know how my story made a difference in your life and you can pass on the spark of hope, love, and healing.

Thank you so much!

NOTES

INTRODUCTION

1. https://lesliepeake.thinkific.com/courses/choose-life-supporting-your-cancer-journey-with-healing-from-the-inside-out
2. **lesliepeake.com/healingbonuses**

4. SOUL ACTIVATION EXERCISE 2: STRONG REASONS FOR LIVING

1. **Adapted from an exercise in Kelly Turner's Book: Radical Remission Surviving Cancer Against All Odds that originally came from, Rick Jarrow: The Ultimate Anti-Cancer Guide: The Inner Path to Finding Your Work in the World.**

1. MAKING YOUR EARTH CONNECTION

1. Anthony Williams, *Life-Changing Foods: Save Yourself and the Ones You Love with the Hidden Healing Powers of Fruits & Vegetables*, 2016, page 57

3. MAKING YOUR HEAVEN CONNECTION

1. http://www.beliefnet.com/inspiration/2004/01/how-to-be-a-survivor.aspx
2. http://www.mindful.org/saki-santorelli/

ABOUT THE PUBLISHER

Red Thread Publishing is an all-female publishing company on a mission to support 10,000 women to become successful published authors and thought leaders. Through the transformative work of writing & telling our stories we are not only changed as individuals, but we are also changing the global narrative & thus the world.

www.redthreadbooks.com

facebook.com/redthreadpublishing
instagram.com/redthreadbooks

Made in the USA
Las Vegas, NV
06 February 2023

66992612R00135